Cascando

and other short dramatic pieces

Other Works By Samuel Beckett
Published By Grove Press

Cascando and Other Short Dramatic Pieces

Film

Endgame

Happy Days

How It Is

Krapp's Last Tape and Other Dramatic Pieces

More Pricks Than Kicks

Murphy

Poems in English

Proust

Stories & Texts for Nothing

Molloy

Malone Dies

The Unnamable

Waiting for Godot

Watt

Samuel Beckett

CASCANDO

and other short dramatic pieces

Grove Press, Inc.

New York

Library of Congress Catalog Card Number: 68-22023
Fifth Printing
Manufactured in the United States of America

DISTRIBUTED BY RANDOM HOUSE, INC., NEW YORK

GROVE PRESS, INC., 196 WEST HOUSTON STREET, NEW YORK, N.Y. 10014

Contents

Cascando

a radio play

translated from the French by the author

music by Marcel Mihalovici

OPENER (*dry as dust*): It is the month of May . . . for me.

Pause.

Yes, that's right.

Pause.

I open.

VOICE (*low, panting*):—story . . . if you could finish it . . .
you could rest . . . you could sleep . . . not before . . .
oh I know . . . the ones I've finished . . . thousands and
one . . . all I ever did . . . in my life . . . with my life
. . . saying to myself . . . finish this one . . . it's the
right one . . . then rest . . . then sleep . . . no more
stories . . . no more words . . . and finished it . . . and
not the right one . . . couldn't rest . . . straight away another . . . to begin . . . to finish . . . saying to myself
. . . finish this one . . . then rest . . . this time it's the
right one . . . this time you have it . . . and finished it
. . . and not the right one . . . couldn't rest . . . straight
away another . . . but this one . . . it's different . . . I'll
finish it . . . then rest . . . it's the right one . . . this
time I have it . . . I've got it . . . Woburn . . . I resume
. . . a long life . . . already . . . say what you like . . . a
few misfortunes . . . that's enough . . . five years later
. . . ten years . . . I don't know . . . Woburn . . . he's
changed . . . not enough . . . recognizable . . . in the
shed . . . yet another . . . waiting for night . . . night
to fall . . . to go out . . . go on . . . elsewhere . . . sleep
elsewhere . . . it's slow . . . he lifts his head . . . now
and then . . . his eyes . . . to the window . . . it's darkening . . . the earth is darkening . . . it's night . . . he gets
up . . . knees first . . . then up . . . on his feet . . . slips

9

out . . . Woburn . . . same old coat . . . right the sea . . . left the hills . . . he has the choice . . . he has only—

OPENER (*with* VOICE): And I close.

Silence.

I open the other.

MUSIC: ....

OPENER (*with* MUSIC): And I close.

Silence.

I open both.

VOICE ⎫
MUSIC ⎭ (*together*): —on . . . it's getting on . . . finish it
....
. . . don't give up . . . then rest . . . sleep . . . not before
....
. . . finish it . . . it's the right one . . . this time you have
....
it . . . you've got it . . . it's there . . . somewhere . . .
....
you've got him . . . follow him . . . don't lose him . . .
....
Woburn story . . . getting on . . . finish it . . . then
....
sleep . . . no more stories . . . no more words . . .
....
come on . . . next thing . . . he—
....

OPENER (*with* VOICE *and* MUSIC): And I close.

Silence.

I start again.

VOICE:—down . . . gentle slope . . . boreen . . . giant aspens
. . . wind in the boughs . . . faint sea . . . Woburn . . .
same old coat . . . he goes on . . . stops . . . not a soul
. . . not yet . . . night too bright . . . say what you like
. . . the bank . . . he hugs the bank . . . same old stick
. . . he goes down . . . falls . . . on purpose or not . . .
can't see . . . he's down . . . that's what counts . . .
face in the mud . . . arms spread . . . that's the idea
. . . already . . . we're there already . . . no not yet
. . . he gets up . . . knees first . . . hands flat . . . in the
mud . . . head sunk . . . then up . . . on his feet . . .
huge bulk . . . come on . . . he goes on . . . he goes
down . . . come on . . . in his head . . . what's in
his head . . . a hole . . . a shelter . . . a hollow . . .
in the dunes . . . a cave . . . vague memory . . .
in his head . . . of a cave . . . he goes down . . . no
more trees . . . no more bank . . . he's changed . . .
not enough . . . night too bright . . . soon the dunes
. . . no more cover . . . he stops . . . not a soul . . . not—

Silence.

MUSIC: . . . .

Silence.

VOICE
MUSIC }(*together*): —rest . . . sleep . . . no more stories
. . . .
. . . no more words . . . don't give up . . . it's the right
. . . .
one . . . we're there . . . nearly . . . I'm there . . .
. . . .
somewhere . . . Woburn . . . I've got him . . . don't
. . . .
lose him . . . follow him . . . to the end . . . come on
. . . .

. . . this time . . . it's the right one . . . finish . . . sleep

. . . .

. . . Woburn . . . come on—

. . . .

Silence.

OPENER: So, at will.
They say, It's in his head.
It's not. I open.

VOICE:—falls . . . again . . . on purpose or not . . . can't see
. . . he's down . . . that's what matters . . . face in the
sand . . . arms spread . . . bare dunes . . . not a scrub
. . . same old coat . . . night too bright . . . say what
you like . . . sea louder . . . like thunder . . . manes of
foam . . . Woburn . . . his head . . . what's in his head
. . . peace . . . peace again . . . in his head . . . no
further . . . to go . . . to seek . . . sleep . . . no . . .
not yet . . . he gets up . . . knees first . . . hands flat . . .
in the sand . . . head sunk . . . then up . . . on his feet
. . . huge bulk . . . same old broad-brim . . . jammed
down . . . come on . . . he's off again . . . ton weight
. . . in the sand . . . knee-deep . . . he goes down . . .
sea—

OPENER (*with* VOICE): And I close.

Silence.

I open the other.

MUSIC: . . . .

OPENER (*with* MUSIC): And I close.

Silence.

So, at will.
It's my life, I live on that.

Pause.

Yes, that's right.

Pause.

What do I open?
They say, He opens nothing, he has nothing to open, it's in his head.
They don't see me, they don't see what I do, they don't see what I have, and they say, He opens nothing, he has nothing to open, it's in his head.
I don't protest any more, I don't say any more, There is nothing in my head.
I don't answer any more.
I open and close.

VOICE:—lights . . . of the land . . . the island . . . the sky . . . he need only . . . lift his head . . . his eyes . . . he'd see them . . . shine on him . . . but no . . . he—

Silence.

MUSIC (*brief*): . . . .

Silence.

OPENER: They say, That is not his life, he does not live on that. They don't see me, they don't see what my life is, they don't see what I live on, and they say, That is not his life, he does not live on that.

Pause.

I have lived on it . . . pretty long.
Long enough.
Listen.

VOICE (*weakening*):—this time . . . I'm there . . . Woburn . . . it's him . . . I've seen him . . . I've got him . . .

come on . . . same old coat . . . he goes down . . . falls
. . . falls again . . . on purpose or not . . . can't see . . .
he's down . . . that's what counts . . . come on—

OPENER (*with* VOICE): Full strength.

VOICE:—face . . . in the stones . . . no more sand . . . all
stones . . . that's the idea . . . we're there . . . this time
. . . no . . . not yet . . . he gets up . . . knees first . . .
hands flat . . . in the stones . . . head sunk . . . then up
. . . on his feet . . . huge bulk . . . Woburn . . . faster . . .
off again . . . he goes down . . . he—

Silence.

MUSIC (*weakening*): . . . .

OPENER (*with* MUSIC): Full strength.

MUSIC: . . . .

Silence.

OPENER: That's not all.
I open both.
Listen.

VOICE ⎫
MUSIC ⎭ (*together*): —sleep . . . no more searching . . . to
. . . .
find him . . . in the dark . . . to see him . . . to say him
. . . .
. . . for whom . . . that's it . . . no matter . . . never
. . . .
him . . . never right . . . start again . . . in the dark . . .
. . . .
done with that . . . this time . . . it's right . . . we're
. . . .
there . . . nearly . . . finish—
. . . .
Silence.

OPENER: From one world to another, it's as though they drew together.

We have not much further to go.

Good.

VOICE } (*together*):   —nearly . . . I've got him . . . I've
MUSIC }

. . . .

seen him . . . I've said him . . . we're there . . . nearly

. . . .

. . . no more stories . . . all false . . . this time . . . it's

. . . .

the right one . . . I have it . . . finish it . . . sleep . . .

. . . .

Woburn . . . it's him . . . I've got him . . . follow him

. . . .

. . . to—

. . . .

Silence.

OPENER: Good.

Pause.

Yes, that's right, the month of May.

You know, the reawakening.

Pause.

I open.

VOICE:—no tiller . . . no thwarts . . . no oars . . . afloat . . .
sucked out . . . then back . . . aground . . . drags free
. . . out . . . Woburn . . . he fills it . . . flat out . . . face
in the bilge . . . arms spread . . . same old coat . . .
hands clutching . . . the gunnels . . . no . . . I don't
know . . . I see him . . . he clings on . . . out to sea . . .
heading nowhere . . . for the island . . . then no more
. . . else—

Silence.

MUSIC: . . . .

Silence.

OPENER: They said, It's his, it's his voice, it's in his head.

Pause.

VOICE:—faster . . . scudding . . . rearing . . . plunging . . .
heading nowhere . . . for the island . . . then no more
. . . elsewhere . . . anywhere . . . heading anywhere . . .
lights—

Silence.

OPENER: No resemblance.
I answered, And that . . .

MUSIC (*brief*): . . . .

Silence.

OPENER: . . . is that mine too?
But I don't answer any more.
And they don't say anything any more.
They have quit.
Good.

Pause.

Yes, the month of May, that's right, the end of May.
The long days.

Pause.

I open.

Pause.

I'm afraid to open.

But I must open.
So I open.

VOICE:—come on . . . Woburn . . . arms spread . . . same old coat . . . face in the bilge . . . he clings on . . . island astern . . . far astern . . . heading out . . . vast deep . . . no more land . . . his head . . . what's in his head . . . Woburn—

OPENER (*with* VOICE): Come on! Come on!

VOICE:—at last . . . no more coming . . . no more going . . . seeking elsewhere . . . always elsewhere . . . we're there . . . nearly . . . Woburn . . . hang on . . . don't let go . . . lights gone . . . of the land . . . all gone . . . nearly all . . . too far . . . too late . . . of the sky . . . those . . . if you like . . . he need only . . . turn over . . . he'd see them . . . shine on him . . . but no . . . he clings on . . . Woburn . . . he's changed . . . nearly enough—

Silence.

MUSIC: . . . .

OPENER (*with* MUSIC): Good God.

MUSIC: . . . .

Silence.

OPENER: Good God good God.

Pause.

There was a time I asked myself, What is it?
There were times I answered, It's the outing.
Two outings.
Then the return.
Where?
To the village.

To the inn.

Two outings, then at last the return, to the village, to the inn, by the only road that leads there.

An image, like any other.

But I don't answer any more.

I open.

VOICE ⎱ (*together*): —don't let go . . . finish . . . it's the
MUSIC ⎰ . . . .
right one . . . I have it . . . this time . . . we're there . . .
. . . .
Woburn . . . nearly—
. . . .

OPENER (*with* VOICE *and* MUSIC): As though they had joined arms.

VOICE ⎱ (*together*): —sleep . . . no more stories . . . come
MUSIC ⎰ . . . .
on . . . Woburn . . . it's him . . . see him . . . say him
. . . .
. . . to the end . . . don't let go—
. . . .

OPENER (*with* VOICE *and* MUSIC): Good.

VOICE ⎱ (*together*): —nearly . . . just a few more . . . a
MUSIC ⎰ . . . .
few more . . . I'm there . . . nearly . . . Woburn . . .
. . . .
it's him . . . it was him . . . I've got him . . . nearly—
. . . .

OPENER (*with* VOICE *and* MUSIC, *fervently*): Good!

VOICE ⎱ (*together*): —this time . . . it's right . . . finish . . .
MUSIC ⎰ . . . .

no more stories . . . sleep . . . we're there . . . nearly . . .
. . . .
just a few more . . . don't let go . . . Woburn . . . he
. . . .
clings on . . . come on . . . come on—
. . . .

Silence.

Words and Music

a radio play

music by John Beckett

MUSIC: *Small orchestra softly tuning up.*

WORDS: Please! (*Tuning. Louder.*) Please! (*Tuning dies away.*) How much longer cooped up here, in the dark? (*With loathing.*) With you! (*Pause.*) Theme . . . (*Pause.*) Theme . . . sloth. (*Pause. Rattled off, low.*) Sloth is of all the passions the most powerful passion and indeed no passion is more powerful than the passion of sloth, this is the mode in which the mind is most affected and indeed—(*Burst of tuning. Loud, imploring.*) Please! (*Tuning dies away. As before.*) The mode in which the mind is most affected and indeed in no mode is the mind more affected than in this, by passion we are to understand a movement of the soul pursuing or fleeing real or imagined pleasure or pain pleasure or pain real or imagined pleasure or pain, of all these movements and who can number them of all these movements and they are legion sloth is the most urgent and indeed by no movement is the soul more urged than by this by this by this to and from by no movement the soul more urged than by this to and—(*Pause.*) From. (*Pause.*) Listen! (*Distant sound of rapidly shuffling carpet slippers.*) At last! (*Shuffling louder. Burst of tuning.*) Hsst!

Tuning dies away. Shuffling louder. Silence.

CROAK: Joe.

WORDS (*humble*): My Lord.

CROAK: Bob.

MUSIC: *Humble muted adsum.*

CROAK: My comforts! Be friends! (*Pause.*) Bob.

MUSIC: *As before.*

CROAK: Joe.

23

WORDS (*as before*): My Lord.

CROAK: Be friends! (*Pause.*) I am late, forgive. (*Pause.*) The face. (*Pause.*) On the stairs. (*Pause.*) Forgive. (*Pause.*) Joe.

WORDS (*as before*): My Lord.

CROAK: Bob.

MUSIC: *As before.*

CROAK: Forgive. (*Pause.*) In the tower. (*Pause.*) The face. (*Long pause.*) Theme tonight . . . (*Pause.*) Theme tonight . . . love. (*Pause.*) Love. (*Pause.*) My club. (*Pause.*) Joe.

WORDS (*as before*): My Lord.

CROAK: Love. (*Pause. Thump of club on ground.*) Love!

WORDS (*orotund*): Love is of all the passions the most powerful passion and indeed no passion is more powerful than the passion of love. (*Clears throat.*) This is the mode in which the mind is most strongly affected and indeed in no mode is the mind more strongly affected than in this.

Pause.

CROAK: *Rending sigh. Thump of club.*

WORDS (*as before*): By passion we are to understand a movement of the soul pursuing or fleeing real or imagined pleasure or pain. (*Clears throat.*) Of all—

CROAK (*anguished*): Oh!

WORDS (*as before*): Of all these movements then and who can number them and they are legion sloth is the LOVE is the most urgent and indeed by no manner of movement is the soul more urged than by this, to and—

Violent thump of club.

CROAK: Bob.

WORDS: From.

Violent thump of club.

CROAK: Bob!

MUSIC: *As before.*

CROAK: Love!

MUSIC: *Rap of baton on stand. Soft music worthy of fore-going, great expression, with audible groans and prot-estations—"No!" "Please" etc.—from* WORDS. *Pause.*

CROAK (*anguished*): Oh! (*Thump of club.*) Louder!

MUSIC: *Loud rap of baton and as before fortissimo, all ex-pression gone, drowning* WORDS' *protestations.*

Pause.

CROAK: My comforts. (*Pause.*) Joe sweet.

WORDS (*as before*): Arise then and go now the manifest un-answerable—

CROAK: *Groans.*

WORDS: . . . to wit this love what is this love that more than all the cursed deadly or any other of its great movers so moves the soul and soul what is this soul that more than by any of its great movers is by love so moved? (*Clears throat. Prosaic.*) Love of woman, I mean, if that is what my Lord means.

CROAK: Alas!

WORDS: What? (*Pause. Very rhetorical.*) Is love the word? (*Pause. Do.*) Is soul the word? (*Pause. Do.*) Do we mean love, when we say love? (*Pause. Do.*) Soul, when we say soul?

CROAK (*anguished*): Oh! (*Pause.*) Bob dear.

WORDS: Do we? (*With sudden gravity.*) Or don't we?

CROAK (*imploring*): Bob!

MUSIC: *Rap of baton. Love and soul music, with just*

audible protestations—"No!" "Please" "Peace" etc.—from WORDS.

Pause.

CROAK (*anguished*): Oh! (*Pause.*) My balms! (*Pause.*) Joe.
WORDS (*humble*): My Lord.
CROAK: Bob.
MUSIC: *Adsum as before.*
CROAK: My balms! (*Pause.*) Age. (*Pause.*) Joe. (*Pause.
Thump of club.*) Joe!
WORDS (*as before*): My Lord.
CROAK: Age!

Pause.

WORDS (*faltering*): Age is . . . age is when . . . old age I
mean . . . if that is what my Lord means . . . is when
. . . if you're a man . . . were a man . . . huddled . . .
nodding . . . the ingle . . . waiting—

Violent thump of club.

CROAK: Bob. (*Pause.*) Age. (*Pause. Violent thump of
club.*) Age!
MUSIC: *Rap of baton. Age music, soon interrupted by
violent thump.*
CROAK: Together. (*Pause. Thump.*) Together! (*Pause.
Violent thump.*) Together, dogs!
MUSIC: *Long la.*
WORDS (*imploring*): No!

Violent thump.

CROAK: Dogs!
MUSIC: *La.*
WORDS (*trying to sing*): Age is when . . . to a man . . .
MUSIC: *Improvement of above.*

WORDS (*trying to sing this*): Age is when to a man . . .
MUSIC: *Suggestion for following.*
WORDS (*trying to sing this*): Huddled o'er . . . the ingle . . .
(*Pause. Violent thump. Trying to sing.*) Waiting for
the hag to put the . . . pan . . . in the bed . . .
MUSIC: *Improvement of above.*
WORDS (*trying to sing this*): Waiting for the hag to put the
pan in the bed . . .
MUSIC: *Suggestion for following.*
WORDS (*trying to sing this*): And bring the . . . arrowroot
. . . (*Pause. Violent thump. As before.*) And bring
the toddy . . .

Pause. Tremendous thump.

CROAK: Dogs!
MUSIC: *Suggestion for following.*
WORDS (*trying to sing this*): She comes in the ashes . . .
(*Imploring.*) No!
MUSIC: *Repeats suggestion.*
WORDS (*trying to sing this*): She comes in the ashes who
loved could not be . . . won or . . .

Pause.

MUSIC: *Repeats end of previous suggestion.*
WORDS (*trying to sing this*): Or won not loved . . . (*wearily*) . . . or some other trouble . . . (*Pause. Trying to sing.*) Comes in the ashes like in that old—
MUSIC: *Interrupts with improvement of this and brief suggestion.*
WORDS (*trying to sing this*): Comes in the ashes like in that
old light . . . her face . . . in the ashes . . .

Pause.

CROAK: *Groans.*

MUSIC: *Suggestion for following.*

WORDS (*trying to sing this*): That old moonlight . . . on the earth . . . again.

Pause.

MUSIC: *Further brief suggestion.*

Silence.

CROAK: *Groans.*

MUSIC: *Plays air through alone, then invites* WORDS *with opening, pause, invites again and finally accompanies very softly.*

WORDS (*trying to sing, softly*):

> Age is when to a man
> Huddled o'er the ingle
> Shivering for the hag
> To put the pan in the bed
> And bring the toddy
> She comes in the ashes
> Who loved could not be won
> Or won not loved
> Or some other trouble
> Comes in the ashes
> Like in that old light
> The face in the ashes
> That old starlight
> On the earth again.

Long pause.

CROAK (*murmur*): The face. (*Pause.*) The face. (*Pause.*) The face. (*Pause.*) The face.

MUSIC: *Rap of baton and warmly sentimental, about one minute.*

Pause.

CROAK: The face.

WORDS (*cold*): Seen from above in that radiance so cold and faint . . .

  Pause.

MUSIC: *Warm suggestion from above for above.*

WORDS (*disregarding, cold*): Seen from above at such close quarters in that radiance so cold and faint with eyes so dimmed by . . . what had passed, its quite . . . piercing beauty is a little . . .

  Pause.

MUSIC: *Renews timidly previous suggestion.*

WORDS (*interrupting, violently*): Peace!

CROAK: My comforts! Be friends!

  Pause.

WORDS: . . . blunted. Some moments later however, such are the powers of recuperation at this age, the head is drawn back to a distance of two or three feet, the eyes widen to a stare and begin to feast again. (*Pause.*) What then is seen would have been better seen in the light of day, that is incontestable. But how often has it not, in recent months, how often, at all hours, under all angles, in cloud and shine, been seen, I mean. And there is, is there not, in that clarity of silver . . . that clarity of silver . . . is there not . . . my Lord . . . (*Pause.*) Now and then the rye, swayed by a light wind, casts and withdraws its shadow.

  Pause.

CROAK: *Groans.*

WORDS: Leaving aside the features or lineaments proper, matchless severally and in their ordonnance—

CROAK: *Groans.*

WORDS: —flare of the black disordered hair as though spread wide on water, the brows knitted in a groove suggesting pain but simply concentration more likely all things considered on some consummate inner process, the eyes of course closed in keeping with this, the lashes . . . (*pause*) . . . the nose . . . (*pause*) . . . nothing, a little pinched perhaps, the lips . . .

CROAK (*anguished*): Lily!

WORDS: . . . tight, a gleam of tooth biting on the under, no coral, no swell, whereas normally . . .

CROAK: *Groans.*

WORDS: . . . the whole so blanched and still that were it not for the great white rise and fall of the breasts, spreading as they mount and then subsiding to their natural . . . aperture—

MUSIC: *Irrepressible burst of spreading and subsiding music with vain protestations—"Peace!" "No!" "Please!" etc.—from* WORDS. *Triumph and conclusion.*

Pause.

WORDS (*gently expostulatory*): My Lord! (*Pause. Faint thump of club.*) I resume, so wan and still and so ravished away that it seems no more of the earth than Mira in the Whale, at her tenth and greatest magnitude on this particular night and shining coldly down —as we say, looking up. (*Pause.*) Some moments later however, such are the powers—

CROAK (*anguished*): No!

WORDS: —the brows uncloud, the lips part and the eyes . . . (*pause*) . . . the brows uncloud, the nostrils dilate, the lips part and the eyes . . . (*pause*) . . . the lips part, a little colour comes back into the cheeks and the eyes . . . (*reverently*) . . . open. (*Pause.*) Then down a little way . . . (*Pause. Change to poetic tone. Low.*)

> Then down a little way
> Through the trash
> To where . . . towards where . . .

Pause.

MUSIC: *Discreet suggestion for above.*
WORDS (*trying to sing this*):

> Then down a little way
> Through the trash
> Towards where . . .

Pause.

MUSIC: *Discreet suggestion for following.*
WORDS (*trying to sing this*):

> All dark no begging
> No giving no words
> No sense no need . . .

Pause.

MUSIC: *More confident suggestion for following.*
WORDS (*trying to sing this*):

> Through the scum
> Down a little way
> To whence one glimpse
> Of that wellhead.

Pause.

MUSIC: *Invites with opening, pause, invites again and finally accompanies very softly.*
WORDS (*trying to sing, softly*):

> Then down a little way
> Through the trash

>   Towards where
>   All dark no begging
>   No giving no words
>   No sense no need
>   Through the scum
>   Down a little way
>   To whence one glimpse
>   Of that wellhead.

(*Pause. Shocked.*) My Lord! (*Sound of club let fall. As before.*) My Lord! (*Shuffling slippers, with halts. They die away. Long pause.*) Bob. (*Pause.*) Bob!

MUSIC: *Brief rude retort.*

WORDS: Music. (*Imploring.*) Music!

Pause.

MUSIC: *Rap of baton and statement with elements already used or wellhead alone.*

Pause.

WORDS: Again. (*Pause. Imploring.*) Again!

MUSIC: *As before or only very slightly varied.*

Pause.

WORDS: *Deep sigh.*

Eh Joe

a television play

Joe, late fifties, grey hair, old dressing-gown, carpet slippers, in his room.

1. *Joe seen from behind sitting on edge of bed, intent pose, getting up, going to window, opening window, looking out, closing window, drawing curtain, standing intent.*

2. *Joe do. (=from behind) going from window to door, opening door, looking out, closing door, locking door, drawing hanging before door, standing intent.*

3. *Joe do. going from door to cupboard, opening cupboard, looking in, closing cupboard, locking cupboard, drawing hanging before cupboard, standing intent.*

4. *Joe do. going from cupboard to bed, kneeling down, looking under bed, getting up, sitting down on edge of bed as when discovered, beginning to relax.*

5. *Joe seen from front sitting on edge of bed, relaxed, eyes closed. Hold, then dolly slowly in to closeup of face. First word of text stops this movement.*

Camera

Joe's opening movements followed by camera at constant remove, Joe full length in frame throughout. No need to record room as whole. After this opening pursuit, between first and final close-up of face, camera has nine slight moves in towards face, say four inches each time. Each move is stopped by voice resuming, never camera move and voice together. This would give position of camera when dolly stopped by first word of text as one yard from maximum close-up of face. Camera does not move between paragraphs till clear that pause (say three seconds) longer than between phrases. Then four inches in say four seconds when movement stopped by voice resuming.

Voice
Low, distinct, remote, little colour, absolutely steady rhythm, slightly slower than normal. Between phrases a beat of one second at least. Between paragraphs about seven, i.e., three before camera starts to advance and four for advance before it is stopped by voice resuming.

Face
Practically motionless throughout, eyes unblinking during paragraphs, impassive except in so far as it reflects mounting tension of listening. *Brief zones of relaxation between paragraphs when perhaps voice has relented for the evening and intentness may relax variously till restored by voice resuming.*

WOMAN'S VOICE:
Joe . . .
(*Eyes open, resumption of intentness.*)
Joe . . .
(*Full intentness.*)
Thought of everything? . . . Forgotten nothing? . . . You're all right now, eh? . . . No one can see you now . . . No one can get at you now . . . Why don't you put out that light? . . . There might be a louse watching you . . . Why don't you go to bed? . . . What's wrong with that bed, Joe? . . . You changed it, didn't you? . . . Made no difference? . . . Or is the heart already? . . . Crumbles when you lie down in the dark . . . Dry rotten at last . . . Eh Joe?

Camera move 1

The best's to come, you said, that last time . . . Hurrying me into my coat . . . Last I was favoured with from

you . . . Say it you now, Joe, no one'll hear you . . .
Come on, Joe, no one can say it like you, say it again
now and listen to yourself . . . The best's to come . . .
You were right for once . . . In the end.

Camera move 2

You know that penny farthing hell you call your mind
. . . That's where you think this is coming from, don't
you? . . . That's where you heard your father . . . Isn't
that what you told me? . . . Started in on you one
June night and went on for years . . . On and off . . .
Behind the eyes . . . That's how you were able to
throttle him in the end . . . Mental thuggee you called
it . . . One of your happiest fancies . . . Mental thuggee
. . . Otherwise he'd be plaguing you yet . . . Then your
mother when her hour came . . . "Look up, Joe, look
up, we're watching you" . . . Weaker and weaker till
you laid her too . . . Others . . . All the others . . . Such
love he got . . . God knows why . . . Pitying love . . .
None to touch it . . . And look at him now . . . Throt-
tling the dead in his head.

Camera move 3

Anyone living love you now, Joe? . . . Anyone living
sorry for you now? . . . That slut that comes on Saturday, you pay her, don't you? . . . Penny a hoist tup-
pence as long as you like . . . Watch yourself you
don't run short, Joe . . . Ever think of that? . . . Eh
Joe? . . . What it'd be if you ran out of us . . . Not
another soul to still . . . Sit there in his stinking old
wrapper hearing himself . . . That lifelong adorer . . .
Weaker and weaker till not a gasp left there either . . .

Is it that you want? . . . Well preserved for his age and the silence of the grave . . . That old paradise you were always harping on . . . No Joe . . . Not for the likes of you.

Camera move 4

I was strong myself when I started . . . In on you . . . Wasn't I, Joe? . . . Normal strength . . . Like those summer evenings in the Green . . . In the early days . . . Of our idyll . . . When we sat watching the ducks . . . Holding hands exchanging vows . . . How you admired my elocution! . . . Among other charms . . . Voice like flint glass . . . To borrow your expression . . . Powerful grasp of language you had . . . Flint glass . . . You could have listened to it for ever . . . And now this . . . Squeezed down to this . . . How much longer would you say? . . . Till the whisper . . . You know . . . When you can't hear the words . . . Just the odd one here and there . . . That's the worst . . . Isn't it, Joe? . . . Isn't that what you told me . . . Before we expire . . . The odd word . . . Straining to hear . . . Why is that, Joe? . . . Why must you do that? . . . When you're nearly home . . . What matter then . . . What we mean . . . It should be the best . . . Nearly home again . . . Another stilled . . . And it's the worst . . . Isn't that what you said? . . . The whisper . . . The odd word . . . Straining to hear . . . Brain tired squeezing . . . It stops in the end . . . You stop it in the end . . . Imagine if you couldn't . . . Ever think of that? . . . If it went on . . . The whisper in your head . . . Me whispering at you in your head . . . Things you can't catch . . . On and off . . . Till you join us . . . Eh Joe?

Camera move 5

How's your Lord these days? . . . Still worth having?
. . . Still lapping it up? . . . The passion of our Joe . . .
Wait till He starts talking to you . . . When you're
done with yourself . . . All your dead dead . . . Sitting
there in your foul old wrapper . . . Very fair health for
a man of your years . . . Just that lump in your bubo
. . . Silence of the grave without the maggots . . . To
crown your labours . . . Till one night . . . "Thou fool
thy soul" . . . Put your thugs on that . . . Eh Joe? . . .
Ever think of that? . . . When He starts in on you . . .
When you're done with yourself . . . If you ever are.

Camera move 6

Yes, great love God knows why . . . Even me . . . But
I found a better . . . As I hope you heard . . . Preferable
in all respects . . . Kinder . . . Stronger . . . More intelligent . . . Better looking . . . Cleaner . . . Truthful
. . . Faithful . . . Sane . . . Yes . . . I did all right.

Camera move 7

But there was one didn't . . . You know the one I
mean, Joe . . . The green one . . . The narrow one . . .
Always pale . . . The pale eyes . . . Spirit made light
. . . To borrow your expression . . . The way they
opened after . . . Unique . . . Are you with me now?
. . . Eh Joe? . . . There was love for you . . . The best's
to come, you said . . . Bundling her into her Avoca
sack . . . Her fingers fumbling with the big horn buttons . . . Ticket in your pocket for the first morning
flight . . . You've had her, haven't you? . . . You've
laid her? . . . Of course he has . . . She went young
. . . No more old lip from her.

Camera move 8

Ever know what happened? . . . She didn't say? . . .
Just the announcement in the *Independent* . . . "On
Mary's beads we plead her needs and in the Holy
Mass" . . . Will I tell you? . . . Not interested? . . .
Well I will just the same . . . I think you should know
. . . That's right, Joe, squeeze away . . . Don't lose
heart now . . . When you're nearly home . . . I'll
soon be gone . . . The last of them . . . Unless that
poor slut loves you . . . Then yourself . . . That old
bonfire . . . Years of that stink . . . Then the silence
. . . A dollop of that . . . To crown all . . . Till His Nibs
. . . One dirty winter night . . . "Mud thou art."

Camera move 9

All right . . . Warm summer night . . . All sleeping . . .
Sitting on the edge of her bed in her lavender slip . . .
You know the one . . . Ah she knew you, heavenly
powers! . . . Faint lap of sea through open window . . .
Gets up in the end and slips out as she is . . . Moon . . .
Stock . . . Down the garden and under the viaduct . . .
Sees from the seaweed the tide is flowing . . . Goes on
down to the edge and lies down with her face in the
wash . . . Cut a long story short doesn't work . . . Gets
up in the end sopping wet and back up to the house
. . . Gets out the Gillette . . . The make you recom-
mended for her body hair . . . Back down the garden
and under the viaduct . . . Takes the blade from the
holder and lies down at the edge on her side . . . Cut
another long story short doesn't work either . . . You
know how she always dreaded pain . . . Tears a strip
from the slip and ties it round the scratch . . . Gets up
in the end and back up to the house . . . Slip clinging

the way wet silk will . . . This all new to you, Joe? . . .
Eh Joe? . . . Gets the tablets and back down the
garden and under the viaduct . . . Takes a few on the
way . . . Unconscionable hour by now . . . Moon going
off the shore behind the hill . . . Stands a bit looking
at the beaten silver . . . Then starts along the edge to
a place further down near the Rock . . . Imagine what
in her mind to make her do that . . . Imagine . . .
Trailing her feet in the water like a child . . . Takes a
few more on the way . . . Will I go on, Joe? . . . Eh
Joe? . . . Lies down in the end with her face a few feet
from the tide . . . Clawing at the shingle now . . . Has
it all worked out this time . . . Finishes the tube . . .
There's love for you . . . Eh Joe? . . . Scoops a little
cup for her face in the stones . . . The green one . . .
The narrow one . . . Always pale . . . The pale eyes . . .
The look they shed before . . . The way they opened
after . . . Spirit made light . . . Wasn't that your description, Joe? . . . (*Voice drops to whisper, almost in-
audible except words in italics.*) All right . . . You've
had the best . . . Now *imagine* . . . Before she goes . . .
Face in the cup . . . Lips on a *stone* . . . Taking Joe
with her . . . Light gone . . . *"Joe Joe"* . . . No sound
. . . To the *stones* . . . Say it now, no one'll hear
you . . . Say "Joe" it parts the *lips* . . . *Imagine* the
hands . . . The *solitaire* . . . Against a *stone* . . . Imagine
the *eyes* . . . Spiritlight . . . Month of June . . . What
year of your Lord? . . . *Breasts* in the stones . . . And
the *hands* . . . Before they go . . . *Imagine* the hands
. . . What are they at? . . . In the *stones* . . .(*Image
fades, voice as before.*) What are they fondling? . . .
Till they go . . . *There's love for you* . . . Isn't it, Joe?
. . . Wasn't it, Joe? . . . *Eh Joe?* . . . Wouldn't you say?
. . . Compared to us . . . Compared to Him . . . *Eh
Joe?* (*Voice and image out.*)

Play

a stage play

Characters

wl First Woman
w2 Second Woman
M   Man

Front centre, touching one another, three identical grey urns (see page 63) about one yard high. From each a head protrudes, the neck held fast in the urn's mouth. The heads are those, from left to right as seen from auditorium, of w2, M, *and* wl. *They face undeviatingly front throughout the play. Faces so lost to age and aspect as to seem almost part of urns. But no masks.*

Their speech is provoked by a spotlight projected on faces alone. See page 62.

The transfer of light from one face to another is immediate. No blackout, i.e., return to almost complete darkness of opening, except where indicated.

The response to light is not quite immediate. At every solicitation a pause of about one second before utterance is achieved, except where a longer delay is indicated.

Faces impassive throughout. Voices toneless except where an expression is indicated.

Rapid tempo throughout.

The curtain rises on a stage in almost complete darkness. Urns just discernible. Five seconds.

Faint spots simultaneously on three faces. Three seconds. Voices faint, largely unintelligible.

45

w1		Yes, strange, darkness best, and the darker the worse, till all dark, then all well, for the time, but it will come, the time will come, the thing is there, you'll see it, get off me, keep off me, all dark, all still, all over, wiped out——
w2	*Together.* *See page 62*	Yes, perhaps, a shade gone, I suppose, some might say, poor thing, a shade gone, just a shade, in the head—(*faint wild laugh*)—just a shade, but I doubt it, I doubt it, not really, I'm all right, still all right, do my best, all I can——
M		Yes, peace, one assumed, all out, all the pain, all as if . . . never been, it will come —(*hiccup*)—pardon, no sense in this, oh I know . . . none the less, one assumed, peace . . . I mean . . . not merely all over, but as if . . . never been——

Spots off. Blackout. Five seconds. Strong spots simultaneously on three faces. Three seconds. Voices normal strength.

w1		I said to him, Give her up——
w2	*Together.*	One morning as I was sitting——
M		We were not long together——

Spots off. Blackout. Five seconds. Spot on w1.

w1: I said to him, Give her up. I swore by all I held most sacred——

Spot from w1 to w2.

w2: One morning as I was sitting stitching by the open window she burst in and flew at me. Give him up, she screamed, he's mine. Her photographs were kind to her. Seeing her now for the first time full length and in the flesh I understood why he preferred me.

Spot from w2 *to* M.

M: We were not long together when she smelled the rat. Give up that whore, she said, or I'll cut my throat— (*hiccup*) pardon—so help me God. I knew she could have no proof. So I told her I did not know what she was talking about.

Spot from M *to* w2.

w2: What are you talking about? I said, stitching away. Someone yours? Give up whom? I smell you off him, she screamed, he stinks of bitch.

Spot from w2 *to* w1.

w1: Though I had him dogged for months by a first-rate man, no shadow of proof was forthcoming. And there was no denying that he continued as . . . assiduous as ever. This, and his horror of the merely Platonic thing, made me sometimes wonder if I were not accusing him unjustly. Yes.

Spot from w1 *to* M.

M: What have you to complain of? I said. Have I been neglecting you? How could we be together in the way we are if there were someone else? Loving her as I did, with all my heart, I could not but feel sorry for her.

Spot from M *to* w2.

w2: Fearing she was about to offer me violence I rang for Erskine and had her shown out. Her parting words, as he could testify, if he is still alive, and has not forgotten, coming and going on the earth, letting people in, showing people out, were to the effect that she would settle my hash. I confess this did alarm me a little, at the time.

Spot from w2 *to* M.

M: She was not convinced. I might have known. I smell her off you, she kept saying. There was no answer to this. So I took her in my arms and swore I could not live without her. I meant it, what is more. Yes, I am sure I did. She did not repulse me.

Spot from M *to* w1.

w1: Judge then of my astoundment when one fine morning, as I was sitting stricken in the morning room, he slunk in, fell on his knees before me, buried his face in my lap and . . . confessed.

Spot from w1 *to* M.

M: She put a bloodhound on me, but I had a little talk with him. He was glad of the extra money.

Spot from M *to* w2.

w2: Why don't you get out, I said, when he started moaning about his home life, there is obviously nothing between you any more. Or is there?

Spot from w2 *to* w1.

w1: I confess my first feeling was one of wonderment. What a male!

Spot from w1 *to* M. *He opens his mouth to speak. Spot from* M *to* w2.

w2: Anything between us, he said, what do you take me for, a something machine? And of course with him no danger of the . . . spiritual thing. Then why don't you get out? I said. I sometimes wondered if he was not living with her for her money.

Spot from w2 *to* M.

M: The next thing was the scene between them. I can't have her crashing in here, she said, threatening to take my life. I must have looked incredulous. Ask Erskine, she said, if you don't believe me. But she threatens to take her own, I said. Not yours? she said. No, I said, hers. We had fun trying to work this out.

Spot from M *to* w1.

w1: Then I forgave him. To what will love not stoop! I suggested a little jaunt to celebrate, to the Riviera or our darling Grand Canary. He was looking pale. Peaked. But this was not possible just then. Professional commitments.

Spot from w1 *to* w2.

w2: She came again. Just strolled in. All honey. Licking her lips. Poor thing. I was doing my nails, by the open window. He has told me all about it, she said. Who he, I said filing away, and what it? I know what torture you must be going through, she said, and I have dropped in to say I bear you no ill-feeling. I rang for Erskine.

Spot from w2 *to* M.

M: Then I got frightened and made a clean breast of it. She was looking more and more desperate. She had a razor in her vanity-bag. Adulterers, take warning, never admit.

Spot from M *to* w1.

w1: When I was satisfied it was all over I went to have a gloat. Just a common tart. What he could have found in her when he had me——

Spot from w1 *to* w2.

w2: When he came again we had it out. I felt like death. He went on and on about why he had to tell her. Too risky and so on. That meant he had gone back to her. Back to that!

Spot from w2 *to* w1.

w1: Pudding face, puffy, spots, blubber mouth, jowls, no neck, dugs you could——

Spot from w1 *to* w2.

w2: He went on and on. I could hear a mower. An old hand mower. I stopped him and said that whatever I might feel I had no silly threats to offer—but not much stomach for her leavings either. He thought that over for a bit.

Spot from w2 *to* w1.

w1: Calves like a flunkey—

Spot from w1 *to* M.

M: When I saw her again she knew. She was looking— (*hiccup*)—wretched. Pardon. Some fool was cutting grass. A little rush, then another. The problem was how to convince her that no . . . revival of intimacy was involved. I couldn't. I might have known. So I

took her in my arms and said I could not go on living
without her. I don't believe I could have.

Spot from M *to* W2.

W2: The only solution was to go away together. He swore
we should as soon as he had put his affairs in order.
In the meantime we were to carry on as before. By
that he meant as best we could.

Spot from W2 *to* W1.

W1: So he was mine again. All mine. I was happy again.
I went about singing. The world——

Spot from W1 *to* M.

M: At home all heart to heart, new leaf and bygones
bygones. I ran into your ex-doxy, she said one night,
on the pillow, you're well out of that. Rather uncalled
for, I thought. I am indeed, sweetheart, I said, I am
indeed. God what vermin women. Thanks to you,
angel, I said.

Spot from M *to* W1.

W1: Then I began to smell her off him again. Yes.

Spot from W1 *to* W2.

W2: When he stopped coming I was prepared. More or
less.

Spot from W2 *to* M.

M: Finally it was all too much. I simply could no
longer——

Spot from M *to* W1.

W1: Before I could do anything he disappeared. That
meant she had won. That slut! I couldn't credit it. I

lay stricken for weeks. Then I drove over to her place. It was all bolted and barred. All grey with frozen dew. On the way back by Ash and Snodland——

Spot from w1 *to* M.

M: I simply could no longer——

Spot from M *to* w2.

w2: I made a bundle of his things and burnt them. It was November and the bonfire was going. All night I smelt them smouldering.

Spot off w2. *Blackout. Five seconds. Spots half previous strength simultaneously on three faces. Three seconds. Voices proportionately lower.*

w1		Mercy, mercy——
w2	*Together.*	To say I am——
M		When first this change——

Spots off. Blackout. Five seconds. Spot on M.

M: When first this change I actually thanked God. I thought, It is done, it is said, now all is going out——

Spot from M *to* w1.

w1: Mercy, mercy, tongue still hanging out for mercy. It will come. You haven't seen me. But you will. Then it will come.

Spot from w1 *to* w2.

w2: To say I am not disappointed, no, I am. I had anticipated something better. More restful.

Spot from w2 *to* w1.

w1: Or you will weary of me. Get off me.

Spot from w1 *to* M.

M: Down, all going down, into the dark, peace is coming, I thought, after all, at last, I was right, after all, thank God, when first this change.

Spot from M *to* w2.

w2: Less confused. Less confusing. At the same time I prefer this to . . . the other thing. Definitely. There are endurable moments.

Spot from w2 *to* M.

M: I thought.

Spot from M *to* w2.

w2: When you go out—and I go out. Some day you will tire of me and go out . . . for good.

Spot from w2 *to* w1.

w1: Hellish half-light.

Spot from w1 *to* M.

M: Peace, yes, I suppose, a kind of peace, and all that pain as if . . . never been.

Spot from M *to* w2.

w2: Give me up, as a bad job. Go away and start poking and pecking at someone else. On the other hand——

Spot from w2 *to* w1.

w1: Get off me! (*Vehement.*) Get off me!

Spot from w1 *to* M.

M: It will come. Must come. There is no future in this.

Spot from M *to* w2.

w2: On the other hand things may disimprove, there is that danger.

Spot from w2 *to* M.

M: Oh of course I know now——

Spot from M *to* wl.

wl: Is it that I do not tell the truth, is that it, that some day somehow I may tell the truth at last and then no more light at last, for the truth?

Spot from wl *to* w2.

w2: You might get angry and blaze me clean out of my wits. Mightn't you?

Spot from w2 *to* M.

M: I know now, all that was just . . . play. And all this? When will all this——

Spot from M *to* wl.

wl: Is that it?

Spot from wl *to* w2.

w2: Mightn't you?

Spot from w2 *to* M.

M: All this, when will all this have been . . . just play?

Spot from M *to* wl.

wl: I can do nothing . . . for anybody . . . any more . . . thank God. So it must be something I have to say. How the mind works still!

Spot from wl *to* w2.

w2: But I doubt it. It would not be like you somehow. And you must know I am doing my best. Or don't you?

Spot from w2 *to* M.

M: Perhaps they have become friends. Perhaps sorrow——

Spot from M *to* w1.

w1: But I have said all I can. All you let me. All I——

Spot from w1 *to* M.

M: Perhaps sorrow has brought them together.

Spot from M *to* w2.

w2: No doubt I make the same mistake as when it was the sun that shone, of looking for sense where possibly there is none.

Spot from w2 *to* M.

M: Perhaps they meet, and sit, over a cup of that green tea they both so loved, without milk or sugar, not even a squeeze of lemon——

Spot from M *to* w2.

w2: Are you listening to me? Is anyone listening to me? Is anyone looking at me? Is anyone bothering about me at all?

Spot from w2 *to* M.

M: Not even a squeeze of——

Spot from M *to* w1.

w1: Is it something I should do with my face, other than utter? Weep?

Spot from w1 *to* w2.

w2: Am I taboo, I wonder. Not necessarily, now that all danger is averted. That poor creature—I can hear her —that poor creature——

Spot from w2 *to* w1.

w1: Bite off my tongue and swallow it? Spit it out? Would that placate you? How the mind works still to be sure!

Spot from w1 *to* M.

M: Meet, and sit, now in the one dear old place, now in the other, and sorrow together, and compare— (*hiccup*) pardon—happy memories.

Spot from M *to* w1.

w1: If only I could think, There is no sense in this . . . either, none whatsoever. I can't.

Spot from w1 *to* w2.

w2: That poor creature who tried to seduce you, whatever became of her, do you suppose?—I can hear her. Poor thing.

Spot from w2 *to* M.

M: Personally I always preferred Lipton's.

Spot from M *to* w1.

w1: And that all is falling, all fallen, from the beginning, on empty air. Nothing being asked at all. No one asking me for anything at all.

Spot from w1 *to* w2.

w2: They might even feel sorry for me, if they could see me. But never so sorry as I for them.

Spot from w2 *to* w1.

w1: I can't.

Spot from w1 *to* w2.

w2: Kissing their sour kisses.

Spot from w2 *to* M.

M: I pity them in any case, yes, compare my lot with theirs, however blessed, and——

Spot from M *to* w1.

w1: I can't. The mind won't have it. It would have to go. Yes.

Spot from w1 *to* M.

M: Pity them.

Spot from M *to* w2.

w2: What do you do when you go out? Sift?

Spot from w2 *to* M.

M: Am I hiding something? Have I lost——

Spot from M *to* w1.

w1: She had means, I fancy, though she lived like a pig.

Spot from w1 *to* w2.

w2: Like dragging a great roller, on a scorching day. The strain . . . to get it moving, momentum coming——

Spot off w2. *Blackout. Three seconds. Spot on* w2.

w2: Kill it and strain again.

Spot from w2 *to* M.

M: Have I lost . . . the thing you want? Why go out? Why go——

Spot from M *to* w2.

w2: And you perhaps pitying me, thinking, Poor thing, she needs a rest.

Spot from w2 *to* w1.

w1: Perhaps she has taken him away to live . . . somewhere in the sun.

Spot from w1 *to* M.

M: Why go down? Why not—

Spot from M *to* w2.

w2: I don't know.

Spot from w2 *to* w1.

w1: Perhaps she is sitting somewhere, by the open window, her hands folded in her lap, gazing down out over the olives——

Spot from w1 *to* M.

M: Why not keep on glaring at me without ceasing? I might start to rave and—(*hiccup*)—bring it up for you. Par——

Spot from M *to* w2.

w2: No.

Spot from w2 *to* M.

M: —don.

Spot from M *to* w1.

w1: Gazing down out over the olives, then the sea, wondering what can be keeping him, growing cold. Shadow stealing over everything. Creeping. Yes.

Spot from w1 *to* m.

m: To think we were never together.

Spot from m *to* w2.

w2: Am I not perhaps a little unhinged already?

Spot from w2 *to* w1.

w1: Poor creature. Poor creatures.

Spot from w1 *to* m.

m: Never woke together, on a May morning, the first to wake to wake the other two. Then in a little dinghy——

Spot from m *to* w1.

w1: Penitence, yes, at a pinch, atonement, one was resigned, but no, that does not seem to be the point either.

Spot from w1 *to* w2.

w2: I say, Am I not perhaps a little unhinged already? (*Hopefully.*) Just a little? (*Pause.*) I doubt it.

Spot from w2 *to* m.

m: A little dinghy——

Spot from m *to* w1.

w1: Silence and darkness were all I craved. Well, I get a certain amount of both. They being one. Perhaps it is more wickedness to pray for more.

Spot from w1 *to* M.

M: A little dinghy, on the river, I resting on my oars, they lolling on air-cushions in the stern . . . sheets. Drifting. Such fantasies.

Spot from M *to* w1.

w1: Hellish half-light.

Spot from w1 *to* w2.

w2: A shade gone. In the head. Just a shade. I doubt it.

Spot from w2 *to* M.

M: We were not civilized.

Spot from M *to* w1.

w1: Dying for dark—and the darker the worse. Strange.

Spot from w1 *to* M.

M: Such fantasies. Then. And now——

Spot from M *to* w2.

w2: I doubt it.

Pause. Peal of wild laughter from w2 *cut short as spot from her to* w1.

w1: Yes, and the whole thing there, all there, staring you in the face. You'll see it. Get off me. Or weary.

Spot from w1 *to* M.

M: And now, that you are . . . mere eye. Just looking. At my face. On and off.

Spot from M *to* w1.

w1: Weary of playing with me. Get off me. Yes.

Spot from w1 *to* M.

M: Looking for something. In my face. Some truth. In my eyes. Not even.

Spot from M *to* w2. *Laugh as before from* w2 *cut short as spot from her to* M.

M: Mere eye. No mind. Opening and shutting on me. Am I as much——

Spot off M. *Blackout. Three seconds. Spot on* M.

M: Am I as much as . . . being seen?

Spot off M. *Blackout. Five seconds. Faint spots simultaneously on three faces. Three seconds. Voices faint, largely unintelligible.*

w1		Yes, strange, etc.
w2	*Together.*	Yes, perhaps, etc.
M		Yes, peace, etc.

Repeat play.

M (*closing repeat*): Am I as much as . . . being seen?

Spot off M. *Blackout. Five seconds. Strong spots simultaneously on three faces. Three seconds. Voices normal strength.*

w1		I said to him, Give her up——
w2	*Together.*	One morning as I was sitting——
M		We were not long together——

Spots off. Blackout. Five seconds. Spot on M.

M: We were not long together——

Spot off M. *Blackout. Five seconds.*

Light

The source of light is single and must not be situated outside ideal space (stage) occupied by its victims.

The optimum position for the spot is at the centre of the footlights, the faces being thus lit at close quarters and from below.

When exceptionally three spots are required to light the three faces simultaneously, they should be as a single spot branching into three.

Apart from these moments a single mobile spot should be used, swivelling at maximum speed from one face to another as required.

The method consisting in assigning to each face a separate fixed spot is unsatisfactory in that it is less expressive of a unique inquisitor than the single mobile spot.

Chorus

w1	Yes strange	darkness best	and the darker	the worse
w2	Yes perhaps	a shade gone	I suppose	some migh
M	Yes peace	one assumed	all out	all the pai
w1	till all dark	then all well	for the time	but it will
w2	poor thing	a shade gone	just a shade	in the hea
M	all as if	never been	it will come	(*hiccup*)
w1	the time will come	the thing is there		you'll see i
w2	(*laugh – – – – –*)	just a shade		but I doub
M	no sense in this	oh I know		none the l
w1	get off me	keep off me	all dark	all still
w2	I doubt it	not really	I'm all right	still all rig
M	one assumed	peace I mean	not merely	all over
w1	all over	wiped out——		
w2	do my best	all I can——		
M	but as if	never been——		

62

Urns

In order for the urns to be only one yard high, it is necessary either that traps be used, enabling the actors to stand below stage level, or that they kneel throughout play, the urns being open at the back.

The sitting posture results in urns of unacceptable bulk and is not to be considered.

Come and Go

dramaticule

for John Calder

Characters

FLO
VI } Age undeterminable
RU

Sitting centre side by side stage right to left FLO, VI, *and* RU. *Very erect, facing front, hands clasped in laps.*

Silence.

VI: Ru.

RU: Yes.

VI: Flo.

FLO: Yes.

VI: When did we three last meet?

RU: Let us not speak.

> *Silence.*
> *Exit* VI *right.*
> *Silence.*

FLO: Ru.

RU: Yes.

FLO: What do you think of Vi?

RU: I see little change. (FLO *moves to centre seat, whispers in Ru's ear. Appalled.*) Oh! (*They look at each other.* FLO *puts her finger to her lips.*) Does she not realize?

FLO: God grant not.

> *Enter* VI. FLO *and* RU *turn back front, resume pose.* VI *sits right. Silence.*

FLO: Just sit together as we used to, in the playground at Miss Wade's.

RU: On the log.

> *Silence.*
> *Exit* FLO *left.*
> *Silence.*

RU: Vi.

VI: Yes.

RU: How do you find Flo?

VI: She seems much the same. (RU *moves to centre seat, whispers in Vi's ear. Appalled.*) Oh! (*They look at each other.* RU *puts her finger to her lips.*) Has she not been told?

RU: God forbid.

> *Enter* FLO. RU *and* VI *turn back front, resume pose.* FLO *sits left. Silence.*

RU: Holding hands . . . that way.

FLO: Dreaming of . . . love.

> *Silence.*
> *Exit* RU *right.*
> *Silence.*

VI: Flo.

FLO: Yes.

VI: How do you think Ru is looking?

FLO: One sees little in this light. (VI *moves to centre seat, whispers in Flo's ear. Appalled.*) Oh! (*They look at each other.* VI *puts her finger to her lips.*) Does she not know?

VI: Please God not.

> *Enter* RU. VI *and* FLO *turn back front, resume pose.* RU *sits right. Silence.*

VI: May we not speak of the old days? (*Silence.*) Of what

came after? (*Silence.*) Shall we hold hands in the old way?

After a moment they join hands as follows: Vi's right hand with Ru's right hand, Vi's left hand with Flo's left hand, Flo's right hand with Ru's left hand, Vi's arms being above Ru's left arm and Flo's right arm. The three pairs of clasped hands rest on the three laps. Silence.

FLO: I can feel the rings.

Silence.

NOTES

Successive positions

1	Flo	Vi	Ru
2	{ Flo		Ru
	{	Flo	Ru
3	Vi	Flo	Ru
4	{ Vi		Ru
	{ Vi	Ru	
5	Vi	Ru	Flo
6	{ Vi		Flo
	{	Vi	Flo
7	Ru	Vi	Flo

Hands

R   u   V   i   Flo

Lighting
Soft, from above only and concentrated on playing area.
Rest of stage as dark as possible.

Costume
Full-length coats, buttoned high, dull violet (RU), dull red
(VI), dull yellow (FLO). Drab nondescript hats with enough
brim to shade faces. Apart from colour differentiation three
figures as alike as possible. Light shoes with rubber soles.
Hands made up to be as visible as possible. No rings
apparent.

Seat
Narrow benchlike seat, without back, just long enough to
accommodate three figures almost touching. As little visible
as possible. It should not be clear what they are sitting on.

Exits
The figures are not seen to go off stage. They should dis-
appear a few steps from lit area. If dark not sufficient to
allow this, recourse should be had to screens or drapes as
little visible as possible. Exits and entrances slow, without
sound of feet.

Ohs
Three very different sounds.

Voices
As low as compatible with audibility. Colourless except for
three "ohs" and two lines following.

Film

This is the original project for *Film*. No attempt has been made to bring it into line with the finished work. The one considerable departure from what was imagined concerns the opening sequence in the street. This was first shot as given, then replaced by a simplified version in which only the indispensable couple is retained. For the rest the shooting followed closely the indications of the script.

The film is divided into three parts. 1. The street (about eight minutes). 2. The stairs (about five minutes). 3. The room (about 17 minutes).

General

Esse est percipi.

All extraneous perception suppressed, animal, human, divine, self-perception maintains in being.

Search of non-being in flight from extraneous perception breaking down in inescapability of self-perception.

No truth value attaches to above, regarded as of merely structural and dramatic convenience.

In order to be figured in this situation the protagonist is sundered into object (O) and eye (E), the former in flight, the latter in pursuit.

It will not be clear until the end of film that pursuing perceiver is not extraneous, but self.

Until end of film O is perceived by E from behind and at an angle not exceeding 45°. Convention: O enters *percipi*=experiences anguish of perceivedness, only when this angle is exceeded.

O not in perceivedness:

O in perceivedness:

E is therefore at pains, throughout pursuit, to keep within this "angle of immunity" and only exceeds it (1) inadvertently at beginning of part one when he first sights O, (2) inadvertently at beginning of part two when he follows O into vestibule and (3) deliberately at end of part three when O is cornered. In first two cases he hastily reduces angle.

Throughout first two parts all perception is E's. E is the camera. But in third part there is O's perception of room and contents and at the same time E's continued perception of O. This poses a problem of images which I cannot solve without technical help. See below, note 8.

The film is entirely silent except for the "ssh!" in part one.

Climate of film comic and unreal. O should invite laughter throughout by his way of moving. Unreality of street scene (see notes to this section).

Outline

1. The street

Dead straight. No sidestreets or intersections. Period: about 1929. Early summer morning. Small factory district. Moderate animation of workers going unhurriedly to work. All going in same direction and all in couples. No automobiles. Two bicycles ridden by men with girl passengers (on crossbar). One cab, cantering nag, driver standing brandishing whip. All persons in opening scene to be shown in some way perceiving—one another, an object, a shop window, a poster, etc., i.e., all contentedly in *percipere* and *percipi*. First view of above is by E motionless and searching with his eyes for O. He may be supposed at street edge of wide (four yards) sidewalk. O finally comes into view hastening blindly along sidewalk, hugging the wall on his left, in opposite direction to all the others. Long dark overcoat (whereas all others in light summer dress) with collar up, hat pulled down over eyes, briefcase in left hand, right hand shielding exposed side of face. He storms along in comic foundered precipitancy. E's searching eye, turning left from street to sidewalk, picks him up at an angle exceeding that of immunity (O's unperceivedness according to convention) (1). O, entering perceivedness, reacts (after just sufficient onward movement for his gait to be established) by halting and cringing aside towards wall. E immediately draws back to close the angle (2) and O, released from perceivedness, hurries on. E lets him get about ten yards ahead and then starts after him (3). Street elements from now on incidental (except for episode of couple) in the sense that only registered in so far as they happen to enter field of pursuing eye fixed on O.

Episode of couple (4). In his blind haste O jostles an elderly couple of shabby genteel aspect, standing on sidewalk, peering together at a newspaper. They should be discovered by E a few yards before collision. The woman is holding a pet monkey under her left arm. E follows O an instant as he hastens blindly on, then registers couple recovering from shock, comes up with them, passes them slightly and halts to observe them (5). Having recovered they turn and look after O, the woman raising a *lorgnon* to her eyes, the man taking off his pince-nez fastened to his coat by a ribbon. They then look at each other, she lowering her *lorgnon*, he resuming his pince-nez. He opens his mouth to vituperate. She checks him with a gesture and soft "sssh!" He turns again, taking off his pince-nez, to look after O. She feels the gaze of E upon them and turns, raising her *lorgnon,* to look at him. She nudges her companion who turns back towards her, resuming his pince-nez, follows direction of her gaze and, taking off his pince-nez, looks at E. As they both stare at E the expression gradually comes over their faces which will be that of the flower-woman in the stairs scene and that of O at the end of film, an expression only to be described as corresponding to an agony of perceivedness. Indifference of monkey, looking up into face of its mistress. They close their eyes, she lowering her *lorgnon,* and hasten away in direction of all the others, i.e., that opposed to O and E (6).

E turns back towards O by now far ahead and out of sight. Immediate acceleration of E in pursuit (blurred transit of encountered elements). O comes into view, grows rapidly larger until E settles down behind him at same angle and remove as before. O disappears suddenly through open housedoor on his left. Immediate acceleration of E who comes up with O in vestibule at foot of stairs.

2. Stairs

Vestibule about four yards square with stairs at inner righthand angle. Relation of streetdoor to stairs such that E's first perception of O (E near door, O motionless at foot of stairs, right hand on banister, body shaken by panting) is from an angle a little exceeding that of immunity. O, entering perceivedness (according to convention), transfers right hand from banister to exposed side of face and cringes aside towards wall on his left. E immediately draws back to close the angle and O, released, resumes his pose at foot of stairs, hand on banister. O mounts a few steps (E remaining near door), raises head, listens, redescends hastily backwards and crouches down in angle of stairs and wall on his right, invisible to one descending (7). E registers him there, then transfers to stairs. A frail old woman appears on bottom landing. She carries a tray of flowers slung from her neck by a strap. She descends slowly, with fumbling feet, one hand steadying the tray, the other holding the banister. Absorbed by difficulty of descent she does not become aware of E until she is quite down and making for the door. She halts and looks full at E. Gradually same expression as that of couple in street. She closes her eyes, then sinks to the ground and lies with face in scattered flowers. E lingers on this a moment, then transfers to where O last registered. He is no longer there, but hastening up the stairs. E transfers to stairs and picks up O as he reaches first landing. Bound forwards and up of E who overtakes O on second flight and is literally at his heels when he reaches second landing and opens with key door of room. They enter room together, E turning with O as he turns to lock the door behind him.

3. The room

Here we assume problem of dual perception solved and enter O's perception (8). E must so manoeuvre throughout what follows, until investment proper, that O is always seen from behind, at most convenient remove, and from an angle never exceeding that of immunity, i.e., preserved from perceivedness.

Small barely furnished room (9). Side by side on floor a large cat and small dog. Unreal quality. Motionless till ejected. Cat bigger than dog. On a table against wall a parrot in a cage and a goldfish in a bowl. This room sequence falls into three parts.

1. Preparation of room (occlusion of windows and mir-

ror, ejection of dog and cat, destruction of print, occlusion of parrot and goldfish).

2. Period in rocking-chair. Inspection and destruction of photographs.

3. Final investment of O by E and dénouement.

1. O stands near door with case in hand and takes in room. Succession of images: dog and cat, side by side, staring at him; mirror; window; couch with rug; dog and cat staring at him; parrot and goldfish, parrot staring at him; rocking-chair; dog and cat staring at him. He sets down case, approaches window from side and draws curtain. He turns towards dog and cat, still staring at him, then goes to couch and takes up rug. He turns towards dog and cat, still staring at him. Holding rug before him he approaches mirror from side and covers it with rug. He turns towards parrot and goldfish, parrot still staring at him. He goes to rocking-chair, inspects it from front. Insistent image of curiously carved headrest (10). He turns towards dog and cat still staring at him. He puts them out of room (11). He takes up case and is moving towards chair when rug falls from mirror. He drops case, hastens to wall between couch and mirror, follows walls past window, approaches mirror from side, picks up rug and, holding it before him, covers mirror with it again. He returns to case, picks it up, goes to chair, sits down and is opening case when disturbed by print, pinned to wall before him, of the face of God the Father, the eyes staring at him severely. He sets down case on floor to his left, gets up and inspects print. Insistent image of wall, paper hanging off in strips (10). He tears print from wall, tears it in four, throws down the pieces and grinds them underfoot. He turns back to chair, image again of its curious headrest, sits down, image again of tattered wall-paper, takes case on

his knees, takes out a folder, sets down case on floor to his left and is opening folder when disturbed by parrot's eye. He lays folder on case, gets up, takes off overcoat, goes to parrot, close-up of parrot's eye, covers cage with coat, goes back to chair, image again of headrest, sits down, image again of tattered wall-paper, takes up folder and is opening it when disturbed by fish's eye. He lays folder on case, gets up, goes to fish, close-up of fish's eye, extends coat to cover bowl as well as cage, goes back to chair, image again of headrest, sits down, image again of wall, takes up folder, takes off hat and lays it on case to his left. Scant hair or bald, to facilitate identification of narrow black elastic encircling head.

When O sits up and back his head is framed in headrest which is a narrower extension of backrest. Throughout scene of inspection and destruction of photographs E may be supposed immediately behind chair looking down over O's left shoulder (12).

2. O opens folder, takes from it a packet of photographs (13), lays folder on case and begins to inspect photographs. He inspects them in order 1 to 7. When he has finished with 1 he lays it on his knees, inspects 2, lays it on top of 1, and so on, so that when he has finished inspecting them all 1 will be at the bottom of the pile and 7—or rather 6, for he does not lay down 7—at the top. He gives about six seconds each to 1–4, about twice as long to 5 and 6 (trembling hands). Looking at 6 he touches with forefinger little girl's face. After six seconds of 7 he tears it in four and drops pieces on floor on his left. He takes up 6 from top of pile on his knees, looks at it again for about three seconds, tears it in four and drops pieces on floor to his left. So on for the others, looking at each again for about three seconds before tearing it up. 1 must be on tougher mount for he has difficulty in tearing it across. Straining hands. He finally

succeeds, drops pieces on floor and sits, rocking slightly, hands holding armrests (14).

3. Investment proper. Perception from now on, if dual perception feasible, E's alone, except perception of E by O at end. E moves a little back (image of headrest from back), then starts circling to his left, approaches maximum angle and halts. From this open angle, beyond which he will enter *percipi*, O can be seen beginning to doze off. His visible hand relaxes on armrest, his head nods and falls forward, the rock approaches stillness. E advances, opening angle beyond limit of immunity, his gaze pierces the light sleep and O starts awake. The start revives the rock, immediately arrested by foot to floor. Tension of hand on armrest. Turning his head to right, O cringes away from perceivedness. E draws back to reduce the angle and after a moment, reassured, O turns back front and resumes his pose. The rock resumes, dies down slowly as O dozes off again. E now begins a much wider encirclement. Images of curtained window, walls, and shrouded mirror to indicate his path and that he is not yet looking at O. Then brief image of O seen by E from well beyond the angle of immunity, i.e., from near the table with shrouded bowl and cage. O is now seen to be fast asleep, his head sunk on his chest and his hands, fallen from the armrests, limply dangling. E resumes his cautious approach. Images of shrouded bowl and cage and tattered wall adjoining, with same indication as before. Halt and brief image, not far short of full-face, of O still fast asleep. E advances last few yards along tattered wall and halts directly in front of O. Long image of O, full-face, against ground of headrest, sleeping. E's gaze pierces the sleep, O starts awake, stares up at E. Patch over O's left eye now seen for first time. Rock revived by start, stilled at once by foot to ground. Hands clutch armrests. O half starts from chair, then stiffens, staring up at E. Gradually

that look. Cut to E, of whom this very first image (face only, against ground of tattered wall). It is O's face (with patch) but with very different expression, impossible to describe, neither severity nor benignity, but rather acute *intentness*. A big nail is visible near left temple (patch side). Long image of the unblinking gaze. Cut back to O, still half risen, staring up, with that look. O closes his eyes and falls back in chair, starting off rock. He covers his face with his hands. Image of O rocking, his head in his hands but not yet bowed. Cut back to E. As before. Cut back to O. He sits, bowed forward, his head in his hands, gently rocking. Hold it as the rocking dies down.

1. First sight of O

2. O released from perceivedness

3. Relation E–O during pursuit

⊢—⊣ = 2 yds

4. The purpose of this episode, undefendable except as a dramatic convenience, is to suggest as soon as possible unbearable quality of E's scrutiny. Reinforced by episode of flower-woman in stairs sequence.

5.

⊢—⊣ =2 yds

6. Expression of this episode, like that of animals' ejection in part three, should be as precisely stylized as possible. The purpose of the monkey, either unaware of E or indifferent to him, is to anticipate behaviour of animals in part three, attentive to O exclusively.

7. Suggestion for vestibule with (1) O in *percipi* (2) released (3) hiding from flower-woman. Note that even when E exceeds angle of immunity O's face never really seen because of immediate turn aside and (here) hand to shield face.

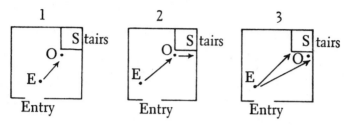

8. Up till now the perceptions of O, hastening *blindly* to illusory sanctuary, have been neglected and must in fact have been negligible. But in the room, until he falls asleep and the investment begins, they must be recorded. And at the same time E's perceiving of O must continue to be given. E is concerned only with O, not with the room, or only incidentally with the room in so far as its elements happen to enter the field of his gaze fastened on O. We see O in the room thanks to E's perceiving and the room itself thanks to O's perceiving. In other words this room sequence, up to the moment of O's falling asleep, is composed of two independent sets of images. I feel that any attempt to express them in simultaneity (composite images, double frame, superimposition, etc.) must prove unsatisfactory. The presentation in a single image of O's perception of the print, for example, and E's perception of O perceiving it—no doubt feasible technically—would per-

haps make impossible for the spectator a clear apprehension of either. The solution might be in a succession of images of different *quality*, corresponding on the one hand to E's perception of O and on the other to O's perception of the room. This difference of quality might perhaps be sought in different degrees of development, the passage from the one to the other being from greater to lesser and lesser to greater definition or luminosity. The dissimilarity, however obtained, would have to be flagrant. Having been up till now exclusively in the E quality, we would suddenly pass, with O's first survey of the room, into this different O quality. Then back to the E quality when O is shown moving to the window. And so on throughout the sequence, switching from the one to the other as required. Were this the solution adopted it might be desirable to establish, by means of brief sequences, the O quality in parts one and two.

This seems to be the chief problem of the film, though I perhaps exaggerate its difficulty through technical ignorance.

9.

Suggestion for room.

This obviously cannot be O's room. It may be supposed it is his mother's room, which he has not visited for many years and is now to occupy momentarily, to look after the pets, until she comes out of hospital. This has no bearing on the film and need not be elucidated.

10. At close of film face E and face O can only be distinguished (1) by different expressions, (2) by fact of O looking up and E down and (3) by difference of ground

(for O headrest of chair, for E wall). Hence insistence on headrest and tattered wall.

11. Foolish suggestion for eviction of cat and dog. Also see note 6.

Door ————————• Dog   1
                    • Cat

O with dog to door
←————————————   2
                    • Cat

Dog out →O back for cat 3
                    • Cat

O with cat to door
←————————————   4
→ Dog back

Cat out →O back for dog 5
                    • Dog

O with dog to door
←————————————   6
→ Cat back

Dog out →O back for cat 7
                    • Cat

O with cat to door
←————————————   8
→ Dog back

Cat out → O back for dog 9
                    • Dog

O with dog to door
←————————————   10
→ Cat back

Dog out →O back for cat 11
                    • Cat

O with cat to door
←————————————   12
→ Dog back

Cat out → O back for dog
                    ————13
                    • Dog

O with dog to door
←————————————   14
→ Cat back

Dog out → O back for cat
                    ————15
                    • Cat

O with cat to door
←————————————   16

Cat and dog → O picks up case
    out   ————————17

12. Chair from front during photo sequence.

13. Description of photographs.

1. Male infant. Six months. His mother holds him in her arms. Infant smiles front. Mother's big hands. Her severe eyes devouring him. Her big old-fashioned beflowered hat.

2. The same. Four years. On a veranda, dressed in loose nightshirt, kneeling on a cushion, attitude of prayer, hands clasped, head bowed, eyes closed. Half profile. Mother on chair beside him, big hands on knees, head bowed towards him, severe eyes, similar hat to 1.

3. The same. 15 years. Bareheaded. School blazer. Smiling. Teaching a dog to beg. Dog on its hind legs looking up at him.

4. The same. 20 years. Graduation day. Academic gown. Mortar-board under arm. On a platform, receiving scroll from Rector. Smiling. Section of public watching.

5. The same. 21 years. Bareheaded. Smiling. Small moustache. Arm round fiancée. A young man takes a snap of them.

6. The same. 25 years. Newly enlisted. Bareheaded. Uniform. Bigger moustache. Smiling. Holding a little girl in his arms. She looks into his face, exploring it with finger.

7. The same. 30 years. Looking over 40. Wearing hat and overcoat. Patch over left eye. Cleanshaven. Grim expression.

14. Profit by rocking-chair to emotionalize inspection, e.g., gentle steady rock for 1 to 4, rock stilled (foot to ground) after two seconds of 5, rock resumed between 5 and 6, rock stilled after two seconds of 6, rock resumed after 6 and for 7 as for 1–4.

Eh Joe was first performed on BBC Television on July 4, 1966.

Play was first performed in German at the Ulmer Theater, Ulm-Donau, Germany, on June 14, 1963.

Film was first shown at the Venice Film Festival on September 4, 1965. The first American showing was at the New York Film Festival on September 14, 1965.

★ "In a stunning first novel, Anderson uses keen observations and vivid imagery to pull readers into the head of an isolated teenager. . . . Yet Anderson infuses the narrative with a wit that sustains the heroine through her pain and holds readers' empathy. . . . But the book's overall gritty realism and Melinda's hard-won metamorphosis will leave readers touched and inspired." —*Publishers Weekly*, Starred Review

★ "An uncannily funny book even as it plumbs the darkness, *Speak* will hold readers from first word to last." —*The Horn Book*, Starred Review

★ "Melinda's voice is distinct, unusual, and very real as she recounts her past and present experiences in bitterly ironic, occasionally even amusing vignettes. . . . Melinda's sarcastic wit, honesty, and courage make her a memorable character whose ultimate triumph will inspire and empower readers." —*Booklist*, Starred Review

"A frightening and sobering look at the cruelty and viciousness that pervade much of contemporary high school life, as real as today's headlines. . . . The plot is gripping and the characters are powerfully drawn . . . a novel that will be hard for readers to forget." —*Kirkus Reviews*, Pointer Review

"Melinda's pain is palpable, and readers will totally empathize with her. This is a compelling book, with sharp, crisp writing that draws readers in, engulfing them in the story." —*School Library Journal*

A story told with acute insight, acid wit, and affecting prose."

—*Library Journal*

"Extremely well-written . . . with a fresh and authentic eye . . . This powerful story has an important lesson: never be afraid to speak up for yourself."

—*VOYA*

A National Book Award Finalist
A Michael L. Printz Honor Book
An Edgar Allan Poe Award Finalist
A *Los Angeles Times* Book Prize Finalist
Winner of the SCBWI Golden Kite Award
An ALA Top Ten Best Book for Young Adults
An ALA Quick Pick
A *Publishers Weekly* Best Book of the Year
A *Booklist* Top Ten First Novel of the Year
A *BCCB* Blue Ribbon Book
A *School Library Journal* Best Book of the Year
A *Horn Book* Fanfare Title
Winner of eight state book awards, Finalist for eleven

Dear Friends,

Twelve years? *Speak* was published twelve years ago?
Not possible.

Sure, I've raised four kids since the book came out. And moved three times. And written six novels. And there are more lines in my face and miles on my bones. But twelve years? No way.

It doesn't seem possible because deep in my heart I am still fourteen. I remember feeling like Melinda so clearly that it shocks me when I look at the year on my driver's license. I remember the excitement, the anxiety, and the confusion. I remember what it feels like to be silenced.

So do many of you.

In the past decade I've spoken to more than half a million high school students about *Speak*. I've lost track of the number of letters and e-mails I've read, and the tears shed on my shoulder by readers who identify with Melinda's struggle. You are hungry to speak up. You just need more adults who will listen.

I'd like to think that, in a small way, *Speak* is helping you find your voices. But *Speak* is just a tool. The real heroes are those of you who have reached down deep—past fear and shame and depression and rage—and found the courage to tell your stories. I have the deepest respect for them.

In her book *The Heart of a Woman*, Maya Angelou wrote, "If one is lucky, a solitary fantasy can totally transform one million realities."

I am beyond lucky. This book has helped a generation of readers take a few steps on their long path to adulthood. You, in turn, have helped me on my own path. I am blessed.

May you always have the courage to speak up.

Laurie

LISTEN

You write to us
from Houston, Brooklyn, Peoria, Rye, NY,
LA, DC, Everyanywhere USA to my mailbox, My
Space Face
Book
A livejournal of bffs whispering
Onehundredthousand whispers to Melinda and
Me.

You:
I was raped, too
sexually assaulted in seventh grade,
tenth grade, the summer after graduation,
at a party
i was 16
i was 14
i was 5 and he did it for three years
i loved him
i didn't even know him.
He was my best friend's brother,
my grandfather, father, mommy's boyfriend,
my date
my cousin
my coach
i met him for the first time that night and—
four guys took turns, and—
i'm a boy and this happened to me, and—

. . . I got pregnant I gave up my daughter for adoption . . .
did it happen to you, too?
U 2?

You:
i wasn't raped, but
my dad drinks, but
i hate talking, but

my brother was shot, but
i am outcast, but
my parents split up, but
i am clanless, but
we lost our house, but
i have secrets—seven years of secrets
and i cut
myself my friends cut
we all cut cut cut
to let out the pain

. . . my 5-year-old cousin was raped—he's beginning to act out
now . . .
do you have suicidal thoughts?
do you want to kill him?

You:
Melinda is a lot like this girl I know
No she's a lot like
(me)
i am MelindaSarah
i am MelindaRogelio i am MelindaMegan,
MelindaAmberMelindaStephenToriPhillipNavdiaTiara-
MateoKristinaBeth
it keeps hurting, but
but
but
but
this book cracked my shell
it keeps hurting I hurt, but
but your book cracked my shell.

You:
I cried when I read it.
I laughed when I read it
is that dumb?
I sat with the girl—
you know, that girl—

I sat with her because nobody sits with her at lunch
and I'm a cheerleader, so there.
speak changed my life
cracked my shell
made me think
about parties
gave me
wings this book
opened my mouth
i whispered, cried
rolled up my sleeves i
hate talking but
I am trying.

You made me remember who I am.
Thanks.

P.S. Our class is gonna analyze this thing to death.

Me:
Me:
Me: *weeping*

With the exception of the first and last stanzas, this poem comes
from lines and words taken from the thousands of letters and
e-mails that Laurie has gotten in the past twelve years.

speak

LAURIE HALSE ANDERSON

SQUARE
FISH

FARRAR STRAUS GIROUX
NEW YORK

I would like to offer my deepest thanks to all the people who read
drafts of this story and encouraged me to keep going:
the Bucks County Children's Writers Group, Marnie Brooks,
Hillary Homzie, Joanne Puglia, Stephanie Anderson,
Meredith Anderson, and Elizabeth Mikesell,
a talented and compassionate editor.
Thank you, thank you.

SQUARE
FISH

An Imprint of Macmillan

Library of Congress Cataloging-in-Publication Data
Anderson, Laurie Halse.
    Speak / Laurie Halse Anderson.
        p. cm.
    Summary: A traumatic event near the end of the summer has a
devastating effect on Melinda's freshman year in high school.
    ISBN 978-0-312-67439-7
    [1. High schools—Fiction.   2. Schools—Fiction.   3. Emotional
problems—Fiction.   4. Rape—Fiction.]   I. Title.

PZ7.A54385Sp   1999
[Fic]—dc21   98-31933

Originally published in the United States by Farrar Straus Giroux
First Square Fish Edition: May 2011
Square Fish logo designed by Filomena Tuosto
Book designed by Filomena Tuosto
macteenbooks.com

10 9 8 7 6 5 4 3 2 1

AR: 4.5 / F&P: Z / LEXILE: 680L

To Sandy Bernstein,
who helped me find my voice,
and to my husband, Greg,
who listens

FIRST MARKING PERIOD

WELCOME TO MERRYWEATHER HIGH

It is my first morning of high school. I have seven new note-books, a skirt I hate, and a stomachache.

The school bus wheezes to my corner. The door opens and I step up. I am the first pickup of the day. The driver pulls away from the curb while I stand in the aisle. Where to sit? I've never been a backseat wastecase. If I sit in the middle, a stranger could sit next to me. If I sit in the front, it will make me look like a little kid, but I figure it's the best chance I have to make eye contact with one of my friends, if any of them have decided to talk to me yet.

The bus picks up students in groups of four or five. As they walk down the aisle, people who were my middle-school lab partners or gym buddies glare at me. I close my eyes. This is what I've been dreading. As we leave the last stop, I am the only person sitting alone.

The driver downshifts to drag us over the hills. The engine clanks, which makes the guys in the back holler something obscene. Someone is wearing too much cologne. I try to open my window, but the little latches won't move. A guy behind me unwraps his breakfast and shoots the wrapper at the back of my head. It bounces into my lap—a Ho-Ho.

We pass janitors painting over the sign in front of the high school. The school board has decided that "Merryweather

High—Home of the Trojans" didn't send a strong abstinence message, so they have transformed us into the Blue Devils. Better the Devil you know than the Trojan you don't, I guess. School colors will stay purple and gray. The board didn't want to spring for new uniforms.

Older students are allowed to roam until the bell, but ninth-graders are herded into the auditorium. We fall into clans: Jocks, Country Clubbers, Idiot Savants, Cheerleaders, Human Waste, Eurotrash, Future Fascists of America, Big Hair Chix, the Marthas, Suffering Artists, Thespians, Goths, Shredders. I am clanless. I wasted the last weeks of August watching bad cartoons. I didn't go to the mall, the lake, or the pool, or answer the phone. I have entered high school with the wrong hair, the wrong clothes, the wrong attitude. And I don't have anyone to sit with.

I am Outcast.

There is no point looking for my ex-friends. Our clan, the Plain Janes, has splintered and the pieces are being absorbed by rival factions. Nicole lounges with the Jocks, comparing scars from summer league sports. Ivy floats between the Suffering Artists on one side of the aisle and the Thespians on the other. She has enough personality to travel with two packs. Jessica has moved to Nevada. No real loss. She was mostly Ivy's friend, anyway.

The kids behind me laugh so loud I know they're laughing about me. I can't help myself. I turn around. It's Rachel, surrounded by a bunch of kids wearing clothes that most definitely did not come from the EastSide Mall. Rachel Bruin, my ex–best friend. She stares at something above my left ear. Words climb up my throat. This was the girl who suffered through Brownies with me, who taught me how to swim, who understood about my parents, who didn't make fun of my bedroom. If there is anyone in the entire galaxy I am dying to tell what really happened, it's Rachel. My throat burns.

Her eyes meet mine for a second. "I hate you," she mouths silently. She turns her back to me and laughs with her friends. I bite my lip. I am not going to think about it. It was ugly, but it's over, and I'm not going to think about it. My lip bleeds a little. It tastes like metal. I need to sit down.

I stand in the center aisle of the auditorium, a wounded zebra in a *National Geographic* special, looking for someone, anyone, to sit next to. A predator approaches: gray jock buzz cut, whistle around a neck thicker than his head. Probably a social studies teacher, hired to coach a blood sport.

Mr. Neck: "Sit."

I grab a seat. Another wounded zebra turns and smiles at me. She's packing at least five grand worth of orthodontia, but has great shoes. "I'm Heather from Ohio," she says. "I'm new here. Are you?" I don't have time to answer. The lights dim and the indoctrination begins.

THE FIRST TEN LIES THEY TELL YOU IN HIGH SCHOOL
1. We are here to help you.
2. You will have enough time to get to your class before the bell rings.
3. The dress code will be enforced.

5

4. No smoking is allowed on school grounds.
5. Our football team will win the championship this year.
6. We expect more of you here.
7. Guidance counselors are always available to listen.
8. Your schedule was created with your needs in mind.
9. Your locker combination is private.
10. These will be the years you look back on fondly.

My first class is biology. I can't find it and get my first demerit for wandering the hall. It is 8:50 in the morning. Only 699 days and 7 class periods until graduation.

OUR TEACHERS ARE THE BEST . . .

My English teacher has no face. She has uncombed stringy hair that droops on her shoulders. The hair is black from her part to her ears and then neon orange to the frizzy ends. I can't decide if she had pissed off her hairdresser or is morphing into a monarch butterfly. I call her Hairwoman.

Hairwoman wastes twenty minutes taking attendance because she won't look at us. She keeps her head bent over her desk so the hair flops in front of her face. She spends the rest of class writing on the board and speaking to the flag about our required reading. She wants us to write in our class journals every day, but promises not to read them. I write about how weird she is.

We have journals in social studies, too. The school must have gotten a good price on journals. We are studying American history for the ninth time in nine years. Another review of map skills, one week of Native Americans, Christopher Columbus in time for Columbus Day, the Pilgrims in time for Thanksgiving. Every year they say we're going to get right up to the present, but we always get stuck in the Industrial Revolution. We got to World War I in seventh grade—who knew there had been a war with the whole world? We need more holidays to keep the social studies teachers on track.

My social studies teacher is Mr. Neck, the same guy who growled at me to sit down in the auditorium. He remembers me fondly. "I got my eye on you. Front row."

Nice seeing you again, too. I bet he suffers from post-traumatic stress disorder. Vietnam or Iraq—one of those TV wars.

SPOTLIGHT

I find my locker after social studies. The lock sticks a little, but I open it. I dive into the stream of fourth-period lunch students and swim down the hall to the cafeteria.

I know enough not to bring lunch on the first day of high school. There is no way of telling what the acceptable fashion will be. Brown bags—humble testament to suburbia, or terminal geek gear? Insulated lunch bags—hip way to save the planet, or sign of an overinvolved mother? Buying is the only solution. And it gives me time to scan the cafeteria for a friendly face or an inconspicuous corner.

7

The hot lunch is turkey with reconstituted dried mashed potatoes and gravy, a damp green vegetable, and a cookie. I'm not sure how to order anything else, so I just slide my tray along and let the lunch drones fill it. This eight-foot senior in front of me somehow gets three cheeseburgers, French fries, and two Ho-Hos without saying a word. Some sort of Morse code with his eyes, maybe. Must study this further. I follow the Basketball Pole into the cafeteria.

I see a few friends—people I used to think were my friends—but they look away. Think fast, think fast. There's that new girl, Heather, reading by the window. I could sit across from her. Or I could crawl behind a trash can. Or maybe I could dump my lunch straight into the trash and keep moving right on out the door.

The Basketball Pole waves to a table of friends. Of course. The basketball team. They all swear at him—a bizarre greeting practiced by athletic boys with zits. He smiles and throws a Ho-Ho. I try to scoot around him.

Thwap! A lump of potatoes and gravy hits me square in the center of my chest. All conversation stops as the entire lunchroom gawks, my face burning into their retinas. I will be forever known as "that girl who got nailed by potatoes the first day." The Basketball Pole apologizes and says something else, but four hundred people explode in laughter and I can't read lips. I ditch my tray and bolt for the door.

I motor so fast out of the lunchroom the track coach would draft me for varsity if he were around. But no, Mr. Neck has cafeteria duty. And Mr. Neck has no use for girls who can run the one hundred in under ten seconds, unless they're willing to do it while holding on to a football.

Mr. Neck: "We meet again."

Me:

Would he listen to "I need to go home and change," or "Did you see what that bozo did"? Not a chance. I keep my mouth shut.

Mr. Neck: "Where do you think you're going?"

Me:

It is easier not to say anything. Shut your trap, button your lip, can it. All that crap you hear on TV about communication and expressing feelings is a lie. Nobody really wants to hear what you have to say.

Mr. Neck makes a note in his book. "I knew you were trouble the first time I saw you. I've taught here for twenty-four years and I can tell what's going on in a kid's head just by looking in their eyes. No more warnings. You just earned a demerit for wandering the halls without a pass."

SANCTUARY

Art follows lunch, like dream follows nightmare. The classroom is at the far end of the building and has long, south-facing windows. The sun doesn't shine much in Syracuse, so the art room is designed to get every bit of light it can. It is dusty in a clean-dirt kind of way. The floor is layered with dry splotches of paint, the walls plastered with sketches of tormented teenagers and fat puppies, the shelves crowded with clay pots. A radio plays my favorite station.

Mr. Freeman is ugly. Big old grasshopper body, like a stilt-walking circus guy. Nose like a credit card sunk between his eyes. But he smiles at us as we file into class.

He is hunched over a spinning pot, his hands muddy red. "Welcome to the only class that will teach you how to survive," he says. "Welcome to Art."

I sit at a table close to his desk. Ivy is in this class. She sits by the door. I keep staring at her, trying to make her look at me. That happens in movies—people can feel it when other people stare at them and they just have to turn around and say something. Either Ivy has a great force field, or my laser vision isn't very strong. She won't look back at me. I wish I could sit with her. She knows art.

Mr. Freeman turns off the wheel and grabs a piece of chalk without washing his hands. "SOUL," he writes on the board. The clay streaks the word like dried blood. "This is where you can find your soul, if you dare. Where you can touch that part of you that you've never dared look at before. Do not come here and ask me to show you how to draw a face. Ask me to help you find the wind."

I sneak a peek behind me. The eyebrow telegraph is flashing fast. This guy is weird. He must see it, he must know what we are thinking. He keeps on talking. He says we will graduate knowing how to read and write because we'll spend a million hours learning how to read and write. (I could argue that point.)

Mr. Freeman: "Why not spend that time on art: painting, sculpting, charcoal, pastel, oils? Are words or numbers more important than images? Who decided this? Does algebra move you to tears?" (Hands raise, thinking he wants answers.) "Can the plural possessive express the feelings in your heart? If you don't learn art now, you will never learn to breathe!!!"

There is more. For someone who questions the value of words, he sure uses a lot of them. I tune out for a while and come back when he holds up a huge globe that is missing half of the Northern Hemisphere. "Can anyone tell me what this is?" he asks. "A globe?" ventures a voice in the back. Mr. Freeman rolls his eyes. "Was it an expensive sculpture that some kid dropped and he had to pay for it out of his own money or they didn't let him graduate?" asks another.

Mr. Freeman sighs. "No imagination. What are you, thirteen? Fourteen? You've already let them beat your creativity out of you! This is an old globe I used to let my daughters kick around my studio when it was too wet to play outside. One day Jenny put her foot right through Texas, and the United States crumbled into the sea. And *voilà*—an idea! This broken ball could be used to express such powerful visions—you could paint a picture of it with people fleeing from the hole, with a wet-muzzled dog chewing Alaska—the opportunities are endless. It's almost too much, but you are important enough to give it to."

Huh?

"You will each pick a piece of paper out of the globe." He walks around the room so we can pull red scraps from the center of the earth. "On the paper you will find one word, the name of an object. I hope you like it. You will spend the rest of the year learning how to turn that object into a piece of art. You will sculpt it. You will sketch it, papier-mâché it, carve it. If the computer teacher is talking to me this year, you can use the lab for computer-aided designs. But there's a catch—by the end of the year, you must figure out how to make your object say something, express an emotion, speak to every person who looks at it."

Some people groan. My stomach flutters. Can he really let us do this? It sounds like too much fun. He stops at my table. I plunge my hand into the bottom of the globe and fish out my paper. "Tree." Tree? It's too easy. I learned how to draw a tree in second grade. I reach in for another piece of paper. Mr. Freeman shakes his head. "Ah-ah-ah," he says. "You just chose your destiny, you can't change that."

He pulls a bucket of clay from under the pottery wheel, breaks off fist-sized balls, and tosses one to each of us. Then he turns up the radio and laughs. "Welcome to the journey."

ESPAÑOL

My Spanish teacher is going to try to get through the entire year without speaking English to us. This is both amusing and useful—makes it much easier to ignore her. She communicates through exaggerated gestures and playacting. It's like taking a class in charades. She says a sentence in Spanish and puts the back of her hand to her forehead. "You have a fever!" someone from class calls out. She shakes her head no, and repeats the gesture. "You feel faint!" No. She goes out to the hall, then bursts through the door, looking busy and distracted. She turns to us, acts surprised to see us, then does the bit with the back of the hand to the forehead. "You're lost!" "You're angry!" "You're in the wrong school!" "You're in the wrong country!" "You're on the wrong planet!"

She tries one more time and smacks herself so hard on the forehead she staggers a bit. Her forehead is as pink as her lipstick. The guesses continue. "You can't believe how many kids are in this class!" "You forgot how to speak Spanish!" "You have a migraine!" "You're going to have a migraine if we don't figure it out!"

In desperation, she writes a sentence in Spanish on the board: *Me sorprende que estoy tan cansada hoy.* No one knows what it says. We don't understand Spanish—that's why we're here. Finally, some brain gets out the Spanish–English dictionary. We spend the rest of the period trying to translate the sen-

tence. When the bell rings, we have gotten as far as "To exhaust the day to surprise."

HOME. WORK.

I make it through the first two weeks of school without a nuclear meltdown. Heather from Ohio sits with me at lunch and
calls to talk about English homework. She can talk for hours.
All I have to do is prop the phone against my ear and "uh-
huh" occasionally while I surf the cable. Rachel and every
other person I've known for nine years continue to ignore me.
I'm getting bumped a lot in the halls. A few times my books
were accidentally ripped from my arms and pitched to the
floor. I try not to dwell on it. It has to go away eventually.

At first, Mom was pretty good about preparing dinners in the
morning and sticking them in the fridge, but I knew it would
end. I come home to a note that says, "Pizza. 555-4892. Small
tip this time." Clipped to the note is a twenty-dollar bill. My
family has a good system. We communicate with notes on the
kitchen counter. I write when I need school supplies or a ride
to the mall. They write what time they'll be home from work
and if I should thaw anything. What else is there to say?

Mom is having staff problems again. My mother manages Effert's, a clothing store downtown. Her boss offered her the
branch at the mall, but she didn't want it. I think she likes
watching the reaction when she says she works in the city.
"Aren't you afraid?" people ask. "I would never work there in

a million years." Mom loves doing the things that other people are afraid of. She could have been a snake handler.

But the downtown location makes it hard to find people to work for her. Daily shoplifters, bums peeing on the front door, and the occasional armed robbery discourage job seekers. Go figure. We are now two weeks into September and she's already thinking Christmas. She has plastic snowflakes and red-felt-wearing Santas on the brain. If she can't find enough employees for September, she'll be in deep doo-doo when the holiday season hits.

I order my dinner at 3:10 and eat it on the white couch. I don't know which parent was having seizures when they bought that couch. The trick to eating on it is to turn the messy side of the cushions up. The couch has two personalities: "Melinda inhaling pepperoni and mushroom" and "No one ever eats in the family room, no ma'am." I chow and watch TV until I hear Dad's Jeep in the driveway. Flip, flip, flip—cushions reversed to show their pretty white cheeks, then bolt upstairs. By the time Dad unlocks the door, everything looks the way he wants to see it, and I have vanished.

My room belongs to an alien. It is a postcard of who I was in fifth grade. I went through a demented phase when I thought that roses should cover everything and pink was a great color. It was all Rachel's fault. She begged her mom to let her do her room over, so we all ended up with new rooms. Nicole refused to put the stupid little skirt around her nightstand and Ivy had gone way over the top, as usual. Jessica did hers in a desert 'n' cowdudes theme. My room was stuck in the middle, a bit stolen from everyone else. The only things that were really mine were my stuffed-rabbit collection from when I was a little kid and my canopy bed. No matter how much Nicole teased me, I wouldn't take the canopy down. I'm thinking about changing the rose wallpaper, but then Mom would get involved and Dad would measure the walls and they would argue about paint color. I don't know what I want it to look like, anyway.

Homework is not an option. My bed is sending out serious nap rays. I can't help myself. The fluffy pillows and warm comforter are more powerful than I am. I have no choice but to snuggle under the covers.

I hear Dad turn on the television. Clink, clink, clink—he drops ice cubes in a heavy-bottomed glass and pours in some booze. He opens the microwave—for the pizza, I guess—slams it closed, then beep-beeps the timer. I turn on my radio so he'll know I'm home. I won't take a real nap. I have this halfway place, a rest stop on the road to sleep, where I can stay for hours. I don't even need to close my eyes, just stay safe under the covers and breathe.

Dad turns up the volume on the TV. The news-team anchor-dude bellows, "Five dead in house fire! Young girl attacked! Teens suspected in gas station holdup!" I nibble on a scab on my lower lip. Dad hops from channel to channel, watching the same stories play over and over.

I watch myself in the mirror across the room. Ugh. My hair is completely hidden under the comforter. I look for the shapes in my face. Could I put a face in my tree, like a dryad from Greek mythology? Two muddy-circle eyes under black-dash eyebrows, piggy-nose nostrils, and a chewed-up horror of a mouth. Definitely not a dryad face. I can't stop biting my lips. It looks like my mouth belongs to someone else, someone I don't even know.

I get out of bed and take down the mirror. I put it in the back of my closet, facing the wall.

OUR FEARLESS LEADER

I'm hiding in the bathroom, waiting for the coast to clear. I peek out the door. Principal Principal spots another errant student in the hall.

Principal Principal: "Where's your late pass, mister?"

Errant Student: "I'm on my way to get one now."

PP: "But you can't be in the hall without a pass."

ES: "I know, I'm so upset. That's why I need to hurry, so I can get a pass."

Principal Principal pauses with a look on his face like Daffy Duck's when Bugs is pulling a fast one.

PP: "Well, hurry up, then, and get that pass."

Errant Student races down hall, waving and smiling. Principal Principal walks the other way, replaying the conversation in his mind, trying to figure out what went wrong. I ponder this and laugh.

FIZZ ED

Gym should be illegal. It is humiliating.

My gym locker is closest to the door, which means I have to change my clothes in a bathroom stall. Heather from Ohio has the locker next to mine. She wears her gym clothes under her regular clothes. After gym she changes out of her shorts but always leaves an undershirt on. It makes me worry about the girls in Ohio. Do they all have to wear undershirts?

The only other girl I know in gym is Nicole. In our old clan, we had never been very close. She almost said something to me when school started, but instead looked down and retied her Nikes. Nicole has a full-length locker in a discreet, fresh-smelling alcove because she's on the soccer team. She doesn't mind changing her clothes in public. She even changes bras, wearing one sports bra to regular class and another to gym class. Never blushes or turns around to hide herself, just changes her clothes. Must be a jock thing. If you're that strong, you don't care if people make comments about your boobs or rear end.

It's late September and we're starting our field hockey unit. Field hockey is a mud sport, played only on wet, cloudy days when it feels like snow. Who dreamed up this one? Nicole is unstoppable at field hockey. She motors downfield so fast she creates a wake of flowing mud that washes over anyone who gets in her way. She does something with her wrist, then the ball is in the goal. She smiles and jogs back to the center circle.

Nicole can do anything that involves a ball and a whistle. Basketball, softball, lacrosse, football, soccer, rugby. Anything. And she makes it look easy. Boys watch her to learn how to play better. It doesn't hurt that she's cute. She chipped her tooth this past summer at some kind of jock camp. Makes her look even cuter.

The gym teachers have a special place in their hearts for Nicole. She shows Potential. They look at her and see future State Championships. Pay raises. One day she scored 35 goals before my team threatened to walk off the field. The gym teacher made her the referee. Not only did my team lose, but four girls went to the nurse with injuries. Nicole doesn't believe in the concept of fouling. She comes from the "play till death or maiming" school of athletics.

If it weren't for her attitude, it would be easier to deal with all this. The crappy locker I have, Heather geeking around me like a moth, cold mornings in the mud watching Nicole, Warrior Princess, listening to the coaches praise her—I could just accept it and move on. But Nicole is so friendly. She even talks to Heather from Ohio. She told Heather where to buy a mouth guard so her braces wouldn't cut up her lips if she got hit with a ball. Heather now wants to buy a sports bra. Nicole is just not a bitch. It would be so much easier to hate her if she were.

FRIENDS

Rachel is with me in the bathroom. Edit that. *Rachelle* is with me in the bathroom. She has changed her name. Rachelle is reclaiming her European heritage by hanging out with the foreign-exchange students. After five weeks in school, she can swear in French. She wears black stockings with runs and doesn't shave under her arms. She waves her hand in the air and you find yourself thinking of young chimpanzees.

I can't believe she was my best friend.

I'm in the bathroom trying to put my right contact lens back in. She's smudging mascara under her eyes to look exhausted and wan. I think about running out so she can't pull the evil eye on me again, but Hairwoman, my English teacher, is patrolling the hall and I forgot to go to her class.

Me: "Hi."

Rachelle: "Mmm."

Now what? I'm going to be completely, totally cool, like nothing has happened. Think ice. Think snow.

Me: "How's it going." I try to put in my contact, and poke myself in the eye. Very cool.

Rachelle: "Eehn." She gets mascara in her eye and rubs it, smearing mascara across her face.

I don't want to be cool. I want to grab her by the neck and shake her and scream at her to stop treating me like dirt. She didn't even bother to find out the truth—what kind of friend is that? My contact folds in half under my eyelid. Tears well in my right eye.

Me: "Ouch."

Rachelle: [Snorts. Stands back from mirror, turns head from side to side to admire the black mess that looks like goose poop across her cheekbones] "*Pas mal.*"

She puts a candy cigarette between her lips. Rachelle wants desperately to smoke, but she has asthma. She has started a new Thing, unheard of in a ninth-grader. Candy cigarettes. The exchange students love it. Next thing you know, she'll be drinking black coffee and reading books without pictures.

An exchange student flushes and comes out of the stall. This one looks like a supermodel with a name like Greta or Ingrid. Is America the only country with dumpy teenagers? She says something foreign and Rachelle laughs. Right, like she understood.

Me:

Rachelle blows a candy cigarette smoke ring at my face. Blows me off. I have been dropped like a hot Pop Tart on a cold kitchen floor. Rachelle and Greta–Ingrid glide out of the bathroom. Neither one of them has toilet paper stuck to her boots. Where is the justice?

I need a new friend. I need a friend, period. Not a true friend, nothing close or share clothes or sleepover giggle giggle yak yak. Just a pseudo-friend, disposable friend. Friend as accessory. Just so I don't feel and look so stupid.

My journal entry for the day: "Exchange students are ruining our country."

HEATHERING

As we ride home on Heather's bus, she tries to bully me into joining a club. She has a Plan. She wants us to join five clubs, one for every day of the week. The tricky part is choosing the clubs that have the Right People. Latin Club is out of the question, as is Bowling. Heather actually likes bowling—it was a big thing in her old school—but she has seen our bowling lanes and she could tell that no Right Person would set foot in there.

When we get to Heather's house, her mother meets us at the door. She wants to hear all about our day, how long I've lived in town, and asks little sideways questions about my parents, so she can figure out if I'm the kind of friend she wants for her daughter. I don't mind. I think it's nice that she cares.

We can't go in Heather's room because the decorators aren't finished. Armed with a bowl of orange popcorn and diet sodas, we retreat to the basement. The decorators finished that first. You can hardly tell it's a basement. It's covered in carpeting nicer than we have in our living room. A monster TV glows in a corner, and there's a pool table and exercise equipment. It doesn't even smell like a basement.

Heather hops on the treadmill and resumes scheming. She isn't finished with her survey of Merryweather's social scene, but she thinks the International Club and the Select Chorus will be a good place to start. Maybe we can try out for the musical. I turn on the television and eat her popcorn.

Heather: "What should we do? What do you want to join? Maybe we should tutor at the elementary school." She increases the speed of the treadmill. "What about your friends from last year? Don't you know Nicole? But she does all those sports, doesn't she? I could never do sports. I fall down too easy. What do you want to do?"

Me: "Nothing. The clubs are stupid. Want some popcorn?"

She edges up the treadmill speed and breaks into a sprint. The treadmill is so loud I can hardly hear the television. Heather wags her finger at me. Hanging back is a common mistake most ninth-graders make, she says. I shouldn't be intimidated. I have to get involved, become a part of the school. That's what all the popular people do. She turns down the treadmill and wipes her brow with a thick towel that hangs off the side of the machine. After a few minutes of cooling down, she hops off. "A hundred calories," she crows. "Want to try?"

I shudder and hold out the popcorn bowl to her. She reaches right past me and takes a pen topped with a Merryweather

Purple ball of fluff off the coffee table. "We must make plans," she says solemnly. She draws four boxes, one for each marking period, then writes "GOALS" in each box. "We won't get anywhere without knowing our goals. Everyone always says that and it is so true." She opens her soda. "What are your goals, Mel?"

I used to be like Heather. Have I changed that much in two months? She is happy, driven, aerobically fit. She has a nice mom and an awesome television. But she's like a dog that keeps jumping into your lap. She always walks with me down the halls chattering a million miles a minute.

My goal is to go home and take a nap.

BURROW

Yesterday Hairwoman yanked me from study hall and forced me to make up my "missing" homework in her room. (She made fluttering noises of concern and mentioned a meeting with my parents. Not good.) Nobody bothered to tell me that study hall was being held in the library today. By the time I find it, the period is almost over. I'm dead. I try to explain to the librarian, but I keep stuttering and nothing comes out right.

Librarian: "Calm down, calm down. It's OK. Don't get upset. You are Melinda Sordino, right? Don't worry. I'll mark you present. Let me show you how it works. If you think you're going to be late, just ask a teacher for a late pass. See? No need for tears."

She holds up a small green pad—my get-out-of-jail-free cards. I smile and try to choke out a "thank you," but can't say anything. She thinks I'm overcome with emotion because she didn't bust me. Close enough. There's not enough time for a nap, so I check out a stack of books to make the librarian happy. I might even read one.

I don't come up with my brilliant idea right then and there. It is born when Mr. Neck tracks me through the cafeteria, demanding my "Twenty Ways the Iroquois Survived in the Forest" homework. I pretend that I don't see him. I cut through the lunch line, loop around a couple making out by the door, and start down a hall. Mr. Neck stops to break up the PDA. I head for the Seniors' Wing.

I am in foreign territory where No Freshman Has Gone Before. I don't have time to worry about the looks I'm getting. I can hear Mr. Neck. I turn a corner, open a door, and step into darkness. I hold the doorknob, but Mr. Neck doesn't touch it. I hear his footsteps lumber down the hall. I feel the wall next to the door until I find a light switch. I haven't stumbled into a classroom; it is an old janitor's closet that smells like sour sponges.

The back wall has built-in shelves filled with dusty textbooks and a few bottles of bleach. A stained armchair and an old-fashioned desk peek from behind a collection of mops and brooms. A cracked mirror tilts over a sink littered with dead roaches crocheted together with cobwebs. The taps are so rusted they don't turn. No janitor has chilled in this closet for a very long time. They have a new lounge and supply room by the loading dock. All the girls avoid it because of the way they stare and whistle softly when we walk by. This closet is abandoned—it has no purpose, no name. It is the perfect place for me.

I steal a pad of late passes from Hairwoman's desk. I feel much, much better.

DEVILS DESTROY

Not only is the Homecoming pep rally going to spring me from algebra, it will be a great time to clean up my closet. I brought some sponges from home. No need to goof off in filth. I want to smuggle in a blanket and some potpourri, too.

My plan is to walk toward the auditorium with the rest of the crowd, then duck in a bathroom until the coast is clear. I would have made it past the teachers with no problem, but I forgot to factor in Heather. Just as the Escape Bathroom comes into sight, Heather calls my name, runs up, and grabs my arm. She is bursting with Merryweather Pride, all perk and pep and purple. And she assumes I am just as happy and excited as she is. We troop down for the brainwashing and she can't stop talking.

Heather: "This is so exciting—a pep rally!! I made extra pom-poms. Here, have one. We'll look great during the Wave. I bet the freshman class has the most spirit, don't you? I've always wanted to go to a pep rally. Can you imagine what it must be like to be on the football team and have the whole school supporting you? That is so powerful. Do you think they'll win tonight? They will, I just know they will. It's been a hard season so far, but we'll get them going, won't we, Mel?"

Her enthusiasm makes me itch, but sarcasm would go right over her head. It won't kill me to go to the rally. I have someone to sit with—that counts as a step up on the ladder of social acceptability. How bad could a rally be?

I want to stand by the doors, but Heather drags me up into the freshman section of the bleachers. "I know these guys," she says. "They work with me on the newspaper."

The newspaper? We have a newspaper?

She introduces me to a bunch of pale, zitty faces. I vaguely recognize a couple; the rest must have gone to the other middle school. I curve up the corners of my mouth without biting my lips. A small step. Heather beams and hands me a pom-pom.

I relax an eensy bit. The girl behind me taps me on the shoulder with her long black nails. She had heard Heather introduce me. "Sordino?" she asks. "You're Melinda Sordino?"

I turn around. She blows a black bubble and sucks it back into her mouth. I nod. Heather waves to a sophomore she knows across the gym. The girl pokes me harder. "Aren't you the one who called the cops at Kyle Rodgers's party at the end of the summer?"

A block of ice freezes our section of the bleachers. Heads snap in my direction with the sound of a hundred paparazzi cameras. I can't feel my fingers. I shake my head. Another girl chimes in. "My brother got arrested at that party. He got fired because of the arrest. I can't believe you did that. Asshole."

You don't understand, my headvoice answers. Too bad she can't hear it. My throat squeezes shut, as if two hands of black fingernails are clamped on my windpipe. I have worked so hard to forget every second of that stupid party, and here I am in the middle of a hostile crowd that hates me for what I had to do. I can't tell them what really happened. I can't even look at that part myself. An animal noise rustles in my stomach.

Heather moves to pat my pom-pom, but pulls her hand back. For a minute she looks like she'll defend me. No, no, she won't. It might interfere with her Plan. I close my eyes. Breathe breathe breathe. Don't say anything. Breathe.

The cheerleaders cartwheel into the gym and bellow. The crowd stomps the bleachers and roars back. I put my head in my hands and scream to let out the animal noise and some of that night. No one hears. They are all quite spirited.

The band staggers through a song and the cheerleaders bounce. The Blue Devil mascot earns a standing ovation by back-flipping right into the principal. Principal Principal smiles and awshucks us. It has only been six weeks since the beginning of school. He still has a sense of humor.

Finally, our own Devils hulk into the gym. The same boys who got detention in elementary school for beating the crap

28

out of people are now rewarded for it. They call it football. The coach introduces the team. I can't tell them apart. Coach Disaster holds the microphone too close to his lips, so all we hear is the sound of his spitting and breathing.

The girl behind me jams her knees into my back. They are as sharp as her fingernails. I inch forward in my seat and stare intently at the team. The girl with the arrested brother leans forward. As Heather shakes her pom-poms, the girl yanks my hair. I almost climb up the back of the kid in front of me. He turns and gives me a dirty look.

The coach finally hands the wet microphone back to the principal, who introduces us to our very own cheerleaders. They slide into synchronized splits and the crowd goes nuts. Our cheerleaders are much better at scoring than the football team is.

CHEERLEADERS

There are twelve of them: Jennie, Jen, Jenna, Ashley, Aubrey, Amber, Colleen, Kaitlin, Marcie, Donner, Blitzen, and Raven. Raven is the captain. Blondest of the blondes.

My parents didn't raise me to be religious. The closest we come to worship is the Trinity of Visa, MasterCard, and American Express. I think the Merryweather cheerleaders confuse me because I missed out on Sunday School. It has to be a miracle. There is no other explanation. How else could they sleep with the football team on Saturday night and be reincarnated as virginal goddesses on Monday? It's as if they operate in two realities simultaneously. In one universe, they are gorgeous, straight-teethed, long-legged, wrapped in designer fashions, and given sports cars on their sixteenth birthdays. Teachers smile at them and grade them on the curve. They know the first names of the staff. They are the Pride of the Trojans. Oops—I mean Pride of the Blue Devils.

In Universe #2, they throw parties wild enough to attract college students. They worship the stink of Eau de Jocque. They rent beach houses in Cancún during Spring Break and get group-rate abortions before the prom.

But they are so cute. And they cheer on our boys, inciting them to violence and, we hope, victory. These are our role models—the Girls Who Have It All. I bet none of them ever stutter or screw up or feel like their brains are dissolving into marshmallow fluff. They all have beautiful lips, carefully outlined in red and polished to a shine.

When the pep rally ends, I am accidentally knocked down three rows of bleachers. If I ever form my own clan, we'll be the Anti-Cheerleaders. We will not sit in the bleachers. We will wander underneath them and commit mild acts of mayhem.

THE OPPOSITE OF INSPIRATION IS . . . EXPIRATION?

For a solid week, ever since the pep rally, I've been painting watercolors of trees that have been hit by lightning. I try to paint them so they are nearly dead, but not totally. Mr. Freeman doesn't say a word to me about them. He just raises his eyebrows. One picture is so dark you can barely see the tree at all.

We are all floundering. Ivy pulled "Clowns" as her assignment. She tells Mr. Freeman she hates clowns; a clown scared her when she was a little girl and it put her into therapy. Mr. Freeman says fear is a great place to begin art. Another girl whines that "Brain" is just too gross a subject for her. She wants "Kittens" or "Rainbows."

Mr. Freeman throws his hands in the air. "Enough! Please turn your attention to the bookshelves." We dutifully turn and stare. Books. This is art class. Why do we need books? "If you are stumped, you may take some time to study the masters." He pulls out an armful. "Kahlo, Monet, O'Keeffe. Pollock, Picasso, Dali. They did not complain about subject, they mined every subject for the root of its meaning. Of course, they didn't have a school board forcing them to paint with both hands tied behind their backs, they had patrons who understood the need to pay for basic things such as paper and paint . . ."

We groan. He's off on the school-board thing again. The school board has cut his supply budget, telling him to make do with the stuff left over from last year. No new paint, no extra paper. He'll rant for the rest of the period, forty-three minutes. The room is warm, filled with sun and paint fumes. Three kids fall dead asleep, eye twitches, snores, and everything.

I stay awake. I take out a page of notebook paper and a pen and doodle a tree, my second-grade version. Hopeless. I crumple it into a ball and take out another sheet. How hard can it be to put a tree on a piece of paper? Two vertical lines for the trunk. Maybe some thick branches, a bunch of thinner branches, and plenty of leaves to hide the mistakes. I draw a horizontal line for the ground and a daisy popping up next to the tree. Somehow I don't think Mr. Freeman is going to find much emotion in it. I don't find any. He started out as such a cool teacher. Is he going to make us thrash around with this ridiculous assignment without helping us?

ACTING

We get a day off for Columbus Day. I go to Heather's house. I wanted to sleep in, but Heather "really, really, really" wanted me to come over. There's nothing on television, anyway. Heather's mom acts very excited to see me. She makes us mugs of hot chocolate to take upstairs and tries to convince Heather to invite a whole group for a sleepover. "Maybe Mellie could bring some of her friends." I don't mention the possibility that Rachel would slit my throat on her new carpet. I show my teeth like a good girl. Her mother pats my cheek. I am getting better at smiling when people expect it.

Heather's room is finished and ready for viewing. It does not look like a fifth-grader's. Or a ninth-grader's. It looks like a commercial for vacuum cleaners, all fresh paint and vacuum-cleaner lines in the carpet. The lilac walls have a few artsy prints on them. Her bookcase has glass doors. She has a television and a phone, and her homework is neatly laid out on her desk. Her closet is opened just a tad. I open it farther with my foot. All her clothes wait patiently on hangers, organized by type—skirts together, pants hanging by their cuffs, her sweaters stacked in plastic bags on shelves. The room screams Heather. Why can't I figure out how to do that? Not that I want my room screaming "Heather!"—that would be too creepy. But a little whisper of "Melinda" would be nice. I sit on the floor flipping through her CDs. Heather paints her nails on her desk blotter and blathers. She is determined to sign up for the musical. The Music Wingers are a hard clan to break into. Heather doesn't have talent or connections—I tell her she is wasting her time to even think of it. She thinks we should try out together. I think she has been breathing too much hairspray. My job is to nod or shake my head, to say "I know what you mean," when I don't, and "That is so unfair," when it isn't.

The musical would be easy for me. I am a good actor. I have a whole range of smiles. I use the shy, look-up-through-the-bangs smile for staff members, and the crinkly-eye smile with a quick shake of my head if a teacher asks me for an answer. If my parents want to know how school went, I flash my eyebrows upward and shrug my shoulders. When people point at me or whisper as I walk past, I wave to imaginary friends down the hall and hurry to meet them. If I drop out of high school, I could be a mime.

Heather asks why I don't think they would let us in the musical. I sip my hot chocolate. It burns the roof of my mouth.

Me: "We are nobody."

Heather: "How can you say that? Why does everyone have that attitude? I don't understand any of this. If we want to be in the musical, then they should let us. We could just stand on-stage or something if they don't like our singing. It's not fair. I hate high school."

She pushes her books to the floor and knocks the green nail polish on the sand-colored carpet. "Why is it so hard to make friends here? Is there something in the water? In my old school I could have gone out for the musical *and* worked on the newspaper *and* chaired the car wash. Here people don't even know I exist. I get squished in the hall and I don't belong anywhere and nobody cares. And you're no help. You are so negative and you never try anything, you just mope around like you don't care that people talk about you behind your back."

She flops on her bed and bursts into sobs. Big boohoos, with little squeals of frustration when she punches her teddy bear. I don't know what to do. I try to soak up the nail polish, but I make the stain bigger. It looks like algae. Heather wipes her nose on the bear's plaid scarf. I slip out to the bathroom and come back with another box of tissues and a bottle of nail-polish remover.

Heather: "I am so sorry, Mellie. I can't believe I said those things to you. It's PMS, don't pay any attention to me. You have been so sweet to me. You are the only person I can trust." She blows her nose loudly and wipes her eyes on her sleeve. "Look at you. You're just like my mom. She says 'No use crying, just get on with your life.' I know what we'll do. First, we'll work our way into a good group. We'll make them like us. By next year, the Music Wingers will be begging us to be in the musical."

It is the most hopeless idea I have ever heard, but I nod and pour the remover on the carpet. It lightens the polish to a bright vomit green and bleaches the carpet surrounding it. When Heather sees what I have done, she bursts into tears again, sobbing that it isn't my fault. My stomach is killing me. Her room isn't big enough for this much emotion. I leave without saying goodbye.

DINNER THEATER

The Parents are making threatening noises, turning dinner into performance art, with Dad doing his Arnold Schwarzenegger imitation and Mom playing Glenn Close in one of her psycho roles. I am the Victim.

Mom: [creepy smile] "Thought you could put one over on us, did you, Melinda? Big high school student now, don't need to show your homework to your parents, don't need to show any failing test grades?"

Dad: [Bangs table, silverware jumps] "Cut the crap. She knows what's up. The interim reports came today. Listen to me, young lady. I'm only going to say this once. You get those grades up or your name is mud. Hear me? Get them up!" [Attacks baked potato.]

Mom: [annoyed at being upstaged] "I'll handle this. Melinda. [She smiles. Audience shudders] We're not asking for much, dear. We just want you to do your best. And we know your best is much better than this. You tested so well, dear. Look at me when I talk to you."

[Victim mixes cottage cheese into applesauce. Dad snorts like a bull. Mom grasps knife.]

Mom: "I said look at me."

[Victim mixes peas into applesauce and cottage cheese. Dad stops eating.]

Mom: "Look at me now."

This is the Death Voice, the Voice that means business. When I was a kid, this Voice made me pee in my pants. It takes more now. I look Mom square in the eye, then rinse my plate and retreat to my room. Deprived of Victim, Mom and Dad holler at each other. I turn up my music to drown out the noise.

BLUE ROSES

After last night's interrogation, I try to pay attention in biology. We are studying cells, which have all these tiny parts you can't see unless you look at them under a microscope. We get to use real microscopes, not plastic Kmart specials. It's not bad.

Ms. Keen is our teacher. I feel kind of sad for her. She could have been a famous scientist or doctor or something. Instead, she's stuck with us. She has wooden boxes all over the front of the room that she climbs on when she talks to us. If she'd cut back on the doughnuts, she'd look like a tiny grandmother doll. Instead, she has a gelatinous figure, usually encased in orange polyester. She avoids basketball players. From their perspective, she must look like a basketball.

I have a lab partner, David Petrakis. Belongs to the Cyber-genius clan. He has the potential to be cute when the braces come off. He is so brilliant he makes the teachers nervous. You'd think a kid like that would get beat up a lot, but the bad guys leave him alone. I have to find out his secret. David ignores me mostly, except when I almost ruined the $300 microscope by twisting the knob the wrong way. That was the day Ms. Keen wore a purple dress with bright blue roses. Baffling. They shouldn't let teachers change like that without some kind of Early Warning Alert. It shakes up the students. That dress was all anyone talked about for days. She hasn't worn it since.

STUDENT DIVIDED BY CONFUSION EQUALS ALGEBRA

I slide into my desk with ten minutes left in algebra class. Mr. Stetman stares at my late pass for a long time. I pull out a clean sheet of paper so I can copy the problems off the board.

I sit in the back row, where I can keep my eye on everyone, as well as whatever is going on in the parking lot. I think of myself as the Emergency Warning System of the class. I plan disaster drills. How would we escape if the chemistry lab exploded? What if an earthquake hit Central New York? A tornado?

It is impossible to stay focused on algebra. It's not that I'm bad at math. I tested at the top of the class last year—that's how I got Dad to pay for my new bike. Math is easy because there is no room for debate. The answer is right or it is wrong. Give me a sheet of math problems and I'll get 98 percent of them right.

But I can't get my head around algebra. I knew why I had to memorize my multiplication tables. Understanding fractions, and decimals, and percentages, and even geometry—all that was practical. Toolz eye kan youz. It made so much sense I never thought about it. I did the work. Made honor roll.

But algebra? Every single day, someone asks Mr. Stetman why we have to learn algebra. You can tell this causes him great personal pain. Mr. Stetman loves algebra. He is poetic about it, in an integral-number sort of way. He talks about algebra the way some guys talk about their cars. Ask him why algebra and he launches into a thousand and one stories why algebra. None of them makes sense.

Mr. Stetman asks if anyone can explain the wangdiddler's role in the negative hotchka theorem. Heather has the answer. She is wrong. Stetman tries again. Me? I shake my head with a sad smile. Not this time, try me again in twenty years. He calls me to the board.

Mr. Stetman: "Who wants to help Melinda understand how we work our way through this problem? Rachel? Great."

My head explodes with the noise of fire trucks leaving the station. This is a real disaster. Rachel/Rachelle clogs up to the board, dressed in an outrageous Dutch/Scandinavian ensemble. She looks half-cute, half-sophisticated. She has red laser eyes that burn my forehead. I wear basic Dumpster togs— smelly gray turtleneck and jeans. I just this minute remember that I need to wash my hair.

Rachelle's mouth moves and her hand glides over the board, drawing funny shapes and numbers. I pull my lower lip all the way in between my teeth. If I try hard enough, maybe I can gobble my whole self this way. Mr. Stetman drones something and Rachelle flutters her eyelids. She nudges me. We are supposed to sit down. The class giggles as we walk back to our seats. I didn't try hard enough to swallow myself.

My brain doesn't think we should spend any time hanging around algebra. We have better things to think about. It's a shame. Mr. Stetman seems like a nice guy.

HALLOWEEN

My parents declare that I am too old to go trick-or-treating. I'm thrilled. This way I don't have to admit that no one invited me to go with them. I'm not about to tell Mom and Dad that. To keep up appearances, I stomp to my room and slam the door.

I look out my window. A group of little creatures is coming up the walk. A pirate, a dinosaur, two fairies, and a bride. Why is it that you never see a kid dressed as a groom on Halloween? Their parents chat at the curb. The night is dangerous, parents are required—tall ghosts in khakis and down jackets floating behind the children.

The doorbell rings. My parents squabble about who will answer it. Then Mom swears and opens the door with a high-pitched "Ooooh, who do we have here?" She must have handed out only one mini-chocolate bar to each creature—their thank-yous do not sound enthusiastic. The kids cut through the yard to the next house and their parents follow in the street.

Last year, our clan all dressed up as witches. We went to Ivy's house because she and her older sister had theatrical makeup. We traded clothes and splurged on cheap black wigs. Rachel and I looked the best. We had used baby-sitting money to rent black satin capes lined in red. We rocked. It was an unusually warm, wicked evening. We didn't need long underwear and the sky was clear. The wind kicked up, skimming clouds over the surface of the full moon, which was hung just to make us feel powerful and strong. We raced through the night, a clan of untouchable witches. I actually thought for a moment that we could cast spells, could turn people into frogs or rabbits, to punish the evil and reward the good. We ended up with pounds of candy. After Ivy's parents went to bed, we lit a candle in the totally dark house. We held it in front of an antique mirror at midnight to see our futures. I couldn't see anything.

This year Rachelle is going to a party thrown by one of the exchange students' host families. I heard her talk about it in algebra. I knew I wouldn't get an invitation. I would be lucky to get an invitation to my own funeral, with my reputation. Heather is walking with some of the little kids in her neighborhood so their mothers can stay home.

I am prepared. I refuse to spend the night moping in my room or listening to my parents argue. I checked out a book from the library, *Dracula*, by Bram Stoker. Cool name. I settle into my nest with a bag of candy corn and the blood-sucking monster.

NAME NAME NAME

In a post-Halloween frenzy, the school board has come out against calling us the Devils. We are now the Merryweather Tigers. Roar.

The Ecology Club is planning a rally to protest the "degrading of an endangered species." This is the only thing talked about at school. Especially during class. Mr. Neck has a steroid rage, screaming about Motivation and Identity and sacred School Spirit. We won't even make it to the Industrial Revolution at this rate.

I get hosed in Spanish. "Linda" means "pretty" in Spanish. This is a great joke. Mrs. Spanish Teacher calls my name. Some stand-up comic cracks, "*No, Melinda no es linda.*"

They call me Me-no-linda for the rest of the period. This is how terrorists get started, this kind of harmless fun. I wonder if it's too late to transfer to German.

I just thought of a great theory that explains everything. When I went to that party, I was abducted by aliens. They have created a fake Earth and fake high school to study me and my reactions. This certainly explains cafeteria food. Not the other stuff, though. The aliens have a sick sense of humor.

THE MARTHAS

Heather has found a clan—the Marthas. She is a freshman member on probation. I have no idea how she did it. I suspect money changed hands. This is part of her strategy to make a place for herself at school. I am supposed to be tagging along. But the Marthas!

It's an expensive clan to run with; outfits must be coordinated, crisp, and seasonally appropriate. They favor plaid for autumn with matching sweaters in colors named after fruit, like apricot and russet apple. Winter calls for Fair Isle sweaters, lined wool pants, and Christmas hair ornaments. They haven't told her what to buy for spring. I predict skirts with geese and white blouses with embroidered ducks on the collar.

I tell Heather she should push the fashion envelope just a teeny bit to be an ironic reflection of the 1950s, you know, innocence and apple pie. She doesn't think the Clan Leaders,

Meg 'n' Emily 'n' Siobhan, understand irony. They like rules too much.

Marthas are big on helping. The name of their group came from somebody in the Bible (the original Martha Clan Leader became a missionary in Los Angeles). But now they follow the Other Martha, Saint Martha of the Glue Gun, the lady who writes books about cheery decorations. Very Connecticut, very prep. The Marthas tackle projects and perform good deeds. This is ideal Heather work. She says they run the canned-food drive, tutor kids in the city, host a walkathon, a danceathon, and a rockingchairathon to raise money for I don't know what. They also Do Nice Things for teachers. Gag.

Heather's first Martha Project is to decorate the faculty lounge for a Thanksgiving party/faculty meeting. She corners me after Spanish and begs me to help her. She thinks the Marthas have given her a deliberately impossible job so they can dump her. I've always wondered what the staff room looks like. You hear so many rumors. Will it have a cot for teachers who need naps? Economy-sized boxes of tissues for emotional melt-downs? Comfortable leather chairs and a private butler? What about the secret files they keep on all the kids?

The truth is nothing more than a small green room with dirty windows and a lingering smell of cigarettes, even though it has been illegal to smoke on school property for years. Metal folding chairs surround a battered table. One wall has a bulletin board that hasn't been cleared off since Americans walked on the moon. And I look, but I can't find any secret files. They must keep them in the principal's office.

I'm supposed to make a centerpiece out of waxed maple leaves, acorns, ribbon, and a mile of thin wire. Heather is going to set the table and hang the banner. She babbles on about her classes while I ruin leaf after red leaf. I ask if we can trade before I cause permanent damage to myself. Heather gently untangles me from the wire. She holds a bunch of leaves in one hand, twists the wire around the stem—one-two—hides the wire with ribbon and hot-glues the acorns into place. It's spooky. I hurry to finish the table.

Heather: "What do you think?"

Me: "You are a decorating genius."

Heather: [eyes rolling] "No, silly. What do you think about this! Me! Can you believe they're letting me join? Meg has been so sweet to me, she calls me every night just to talk." She walks around the table and straightens the forks I just set. "You are going to think this is ridiculous, but I was so upset last month I asked my parents to send me to boarding school. But now I have friends, and I know how to open my locker, and [she pauses and scrunches her face up] it's just perfect!"

I don't have to choke out an answer because Meg 'n' Emily 'n' Siobhan march in, carrying trays of mini-muffins and apple slices dipped in chocolate. Meg raises an eyebrow at me.

Me: "Thanks for the homework, Heather. You are so helpful." I scoot out the door, leaving it open a crack to watch what happens next. Heather stands at attention while our handiwork is inspected. Meg picks up the centerpiece and examines it from every angle.

Meg: "Nice job."

Heather blushes.

Emily: "Who was that girl?"

Heather: "She's a friend. She was the first person to make me feel at home here."

Siobhan: "She's creepy. What's wrong with her lips? It looks like she's got a disease or something."

Emily holds out her watch (the watchband matches the bow in her hair). Five minutes. Heather has to leave before the teachers arrive. Part of being on probation means she's not allowed to take credit for her work.

I hide in the bathroom until I know Heather's bus has left. The salt in my tears feels good when it stings my lips. I wash my face in the sink until there is nothing left of it, no eyes, no nose, no mouth. A slick nothing.

NIGHTMARE

I see IT in the hallway. IT goes to Merryweather. IT is walking with Aubrey Cheerleader. IT is my nightmare and I can't wake up.

IT sees me. IT smiles and winks. Good thing my lips are stitched together or I'd throw up.

MY REPORT CARD:

Plays Nice	B	Social Studies	C	Spanish	C	Art	A
Lunch	D	Biology	B	Algebra	C+		
Clothes	C	English	C	Gym	C+		

SECOND MARKING PERIOD

GO _____ (FILL IN THE BLANK)!

The Ecology Club has won round two. We are no longer the Tigers because the name shows "shocking disrespect" for an endangered creature.

I know I'm shocked.

The Ecology Club made great posters. They laid out headlines from the sports page: TIGERS RIPPED APART! TIGERS SLAUGHTERED! TIGERS KILLED! side by side with color photos of Bengal tigers with their skins peeled off. Effective. The Ecology Club has some good PR people. (The football team would have protested, but the sad truth is that they've lost every game this season. They are happy not to be called the Tigers. Other teams called them Pussycats. Not manly.) More than half the school signed a petition and the tree huggers got letters of support from a bunch of outside groups and three Hollywood Actors.

They herd us into an assembly that is supposed to be a "democratic forum" to come up with a new school mascot. Who are we? We can't be the Buccaneers because pirates supported violence and discrimination against women. The kid who suggests the Shoemakers in honor of the old moccasin factory is laughed out of the auditorium. Warriors insults Native Americans. I think Overbearing Eurocentric Patriarchs would be perfect, but I don't suggest it.

Student Council is holding an election before Winter Break.
Our choices:

    a. The Bees—useful to agriculture, painful to cross

    b. Icebergs—in honor of our festive winter weather

    c. Hilltoppers—guaranteed to frighten opponents

    d. Wombats—no one knows if they're endangered

CLOSET SPACE

My parents commanded me to stay after school every day for
extra help from teachers. I agreed to stay after school. I hang
out in my refurbished closet. It is shaping up nicely.

The first thing to go is the mirror. It is screwed to the wall, so I
cover it with a poster of Maya Angelou that the librarian gave
me. She said Ms. Angelou is one of the greatest American writers. The poster was coming down because the school board
banned one of her books. She must be a great writer if the
school board is afraid of her. Maya Angelou's picture watches
me while I sweep and mop the floor, while I scrub the shelves,
while I chase spiders out of the corners. I do a little bit of work
every day. It's like building a fort. I figure Maya would like it if
I read in here, so I bring a few books from home. Mostly I
watch the scary movies playing on the inside of my eyelids.

It is getting harder to talk. My throat is always sore, my lips
raw. When I wake up in the morning, my jaws are clenched so
tight I have a headache. Sometimes my mouth relaxes around
Heather, if we're alone. Every time I try to talk to my parents

or a teacher, I sputter or freeze. What is wrong with me? It's like I have some kind of spastic laryngitis.

I know my head isn't screwed on straight. I want to leave, transfer, warp myself to another galaxy. I want to confess everything, hand over the guilt and mistake and anger to someone else. There is a beast in my gut, I can hear it scraping away at the inside of my ribs. Even if I dump the memory, it will stay with me, staining me. My closet is a good thing, a quiet place that helps me hold these thoughts inside my head where no one can hear them.

ALL TOGETHER NOW

My Spanish teacher breaks the "no English" rule to tell us that we had better stop pretending we don't understand the homework assignments or we're all going to get detention. Then she repeats what she just said in Spanish, though it seems as if she tosses in a few extra phrases. I don't know why she hasn't figured it out yet. If she just taught us all the swear-words the first day, we would have done whatever she wanted the rest of the year.

Detention does not sound appealing. I do my homework—choose five verbs and conjugate them.
To translate: *traducir*. I traducate.
To flunk: *fracasar*. Yo am almost fracasaring.
To hide: *esconder*. To escape: *escapar*.
To forget: *olvidar*.

JOB DAY

Just in case we forget that "wearehere to getagood foundation-sowecangoto college live up to our potential getagood job live happily ever after and goto DisneyWorld," we have a Job Day.

Like all things Hi!School, it starts with a test, a test of my desires and my dreams. Do I (a) prefer to spend time with a large group of people? (b) prefer to spend time with a small group of close friends? (c) prefer to spend time with family? (d) prefer to spend time alone?

Am I (a) a helper? (b) a doer? (c) a planner? (d) a dreamer?

If I were tied to railroad tracks and the 3:15 train to Rochester was ready to cut a path across my middle, would I (a) scream for help? (b) ask my little mice friends to chew through the ropes? (c) remember that my favorite jeans were in the dryer and were hopelessly wrinkled? (d) close my eyes and pretend nothing was wrong?

Two hundred questions later, I get my results. I should consider a career in (a) forestry (b) firefighting (c) communications (d) mortuary science. Heather's results are clearer. She should be a nurse. It makes her jump up and down.

Heather: "This is the best! I know exactly what I'm going to do. I'll be a candy striper at the hospital this summer. Why don't you do it with me? I'll study real hard in biology and go to S.U. and get my R.N. What a great plan!"

How could she know this? I don't know what I'm doing in the next five minutes and she has the next ten years figured out. I'll worry about making it out of ninth grade alive. Then I'll think about a career path.

FIRST AMENDMENT

Mr. Neck storms into class, a bull chasing thirty-three red flags. We slide into our seats. I think for sure he's going to explode. Which he does, but in an unpredictable, faintly educational way.

IMMIGRATION. He writes it on the board. I'm pretty sure he spelled it right.

Mr. Neck: "My family has been in this country for over two hundred years. We built this place, fought in every war from the first one to the last one, paid taxes, and voted."

A cartoon thought bubble forms over the heads of everyone in the class. ("WILL THIS BE ON THE TEST?")

Mr. Neck: "So tell me why my son can't get a job."

A few hands creep skyward. Mr. Neck ignores them. It is a pretend question, one he asked so he could give the answer. I relax. This is like when my father complains about his boss. The best thing to do is to stay awake and blink sympathetically.

His son wanted to be a firefighter, but didn't get the job. Mr. Neck is convinced that this is some kind of reverse discrimination. He says we should close our borders so that real Americans can get the jobs they deserve. The job test said that I would be a good firefighter. I wonder if I could take a job away from Mr. Neck's son.

I tune out and focus on my doodle, a pine tree. I've been trying to carve a linoleum block in art class. The problem with the block is that there is no way to correct mistakes. Every mistake I make is frozen in the picture. So I have to think ahead.

Mr. Neck writes on the board again: "DEBATE: America should have closed her borders in 1900." That strikes a nerve. Several nerves. I can see kids counting backward on their fingers, trying to figure when their grandparents or great-grandparents were born, when they came to America, if they would have made the Neck Cut. When they figure out they would have been stuck in a country that hated them, or a place with no schools, or a place with no future, their hands shoot up. They beg to differ with Mr. Neck's learned opinion.

I don't know where my family came from. Someplace cold, where they eat beans on Thursday and hang their wash on the line on Monday. I don't know how long we've been in America. We've been in this school district since I was in first grade; that must count for something. I start an apple tree.

The arguments jump back and forth across the room. A few suck-ups quickly figure out which side Mr. Neck is squatting on, so they fight to throw out the "foreigners." Anyone whose family immigrated in the last century has a story to tell about how hard their relatives have worked, the contributions they make to the country, the taxes they pay. A member of the Archery Club tries to say that we are all foreigners and we should give the country back to the Native Americans, but she's buried under disagreement. Mr. Neck enjoys the noise, until one kid challenges him directly.

Brave Kid: "Maybe your son didn't get that job because he's not good enough. Or he's lazy. Or the other guy was better than him, no matter what his skin color. I think the white people who have been here for two hundred years are the ones pulling down the country. They don't know how to work— they've had it too easy."

The pro-immigration forces erupt in applause and hooting.

Mr. Neck. "You watch your mouth, mister. You are talking about my son. I don't want to hear any more from you. That's enough debate—get your books out."

The Neck is back in control. Show time is over. I try to draw a branch coming out of a tree trunk for the 315th time. It looks so flat, a cheap, cruddy drawing. I have no idea how to make it come alive. I am so focused I don't notice at first that

David Petrakis My Lab Partner has stood up. The class stops talking. I put my pencil down.

Mr. Neck: "Mr. Petrakis, take your seat."

David Petrakis is never, ever in trouble. He is the kid who wins perfect attendance records, who helps the staff chase down bugs in the computer files of report cards. I chew a hangnail on my pinkie. What is he thinking? Has he flipped, finally cracked under the pressure of being smarter than everyone?

David: "If the class is debating, then each student has the right to say what's on his mind."

Mr. Neck: "I decide who talks in here."

David: "You opened a debate. You can't close it just because it is not going your way."

Mr. Neck: "Watch me. Take your seat, Mr. Petrakis."

David: "The Constitution does not recognize different classes of citizenship based on time spent living in the country. I am a citizen, with the same rights as your son, or you. As a citizen, and as a student, I am protesting the tone of this lesson as racist, intolerant, and xenophobic."

Mr. Neck: "Sit your butt in that chair, Petrakis, and watch your mouth! I try to get a debate going in here and you people turn it into a race thing. Sit down or you're going to the principal."

David stares at Mr. Neck, looks at the flag for a minute, then picks up his books and walks out of the room. He says a million things without saying a word. I make a note to study David Petrakis. I have never heard a more eloquent silence.

GIVING THANKS

The Pilgrims gave thanks at Thanksgiving because the Native Americans saved their sorry butts from starving. I give thanks at Thanksgiving because my mother finally goes to work and my father orders pizza.

My normally harried, rushed mother always turns into a strung-out retail junkie just before Turkey Day. It's because of Black Friday, the day after Thanksgiving, the start of the Christmas shopping season. If she doesn't sell a billion shirts and twelve million belts on Black Friday, the world will end. She lives on cigarettes and black coffee, swearing like a rap star and calculating spreadsheets in her head. The goals she sets for her store are totally unrealistic and she knows it. She can't help herself. It's like watching someone caught in an electric fence, twitching and squirming and very stuck. Every year, just when she's stressed to the snapping point, she cooks Thanksgiving dinner. We beg her not to. We plead with her, send anonymous notes. She doesn't listen.

I go to bed the night before Thanksgiving at 10 p.m. She's pounding on her laptop at the dining-room table. When I come downstairs Thanksgiving morning, she's still there. I don't think she slept.

She looks up at me in my robe and bunny slippers. "Oh, damn," she says. "The turkey."

I peel potatoes while she gives the frozen turkey a hot bath. The windows fog up, separating us from the outside. I want to suggest that we have something else for dinner, spaghetti maybe, or sandwiches, but I know she wouldn't take it the right way. She hacks at the guts of the turkey with an ice pick to get out the bag of body parts. I'm impressed. Last year she cooked the bird with the bag inside.

Cooking Thanksgiving dinner means something to her. It's like a holy obligation, part of what makes her a wife and mother. My family doesn't talk much and we have nothing in common, but if my mother cooks a proper Thanksgiving dinner, it says we'll be a family for one more year. Kodak logic. Only in film commercials does stuff like that work.

I finish the potatoes. She sends me to the TV to watch the parades. Dad stumbles downstairs. "How is she?" he asks before he goes in the kitchen. "It's Thanksgiving," I say. Dad puts on his coat. "Doughnuts?" he asks. I nod.

The phone rings. Mom answers. It's the store. Emergency #1. I go into the kitchen for a soda. She pours me orange juice, which I can't drink because it burns my scabby lips. The turkey floats in the sink, a ten-pound turkey iceberg. A turkeyberg. I feel very much like the *Titanic*.

Mom hangs up and chases me out with instructions to take a shower and clean my room. I soak in the bathtub. I fill my lungs with air and float on top of the water, then blow out all my breath and sink to the bottom. I put my head under-water to listen to my heart beat. The phone rings again. Emergency #2.

By the time I'm dressed, the parades are over and Dad is watching football. Confectioner's sugar dusts the stubble on his face. I don't like it when he bums around the house on hol-idays. I like my Dad clean-shaven and wearing a suit. He mo-tions for me to get out of the way so he can see the screen.

Mom is on the phone. Emergency #3. The long curly cord snakes around and around her thin body, like a rope tying her to the stake. Two drumstick tips poke out of an enormous pot of boiling water. She is boiling the frozen turkey. "It's too big for the microwave," she explains. "It will be thawed soon." She puts a finger in her free ear to concentrate on what the phone is telling her. I take a plain doughnut from the bag and go back to my room.

Three magazines later, my parents are arguing. Not a rip-roarer. A simmering argument, a few bubbles splashing on the stove. I want another doughnut, but don't feel like wading through the fight to get it. They retreat to their corners when the phone rings again. Here's my chance.

Mom has the phone to her ear when I walk in the kitchen, but she isn't listening to it. She rubs the steam from the window and stares into the back yard. I join her at the sink.

Dad strides across the back yard, wearing an oven mitt and carrying the steaming turkey by one leg. "He said it would take hours to thaw," mutters Mom. A tiny voice squeaks from the receiver. "No, not you, Ted," she tells the phone. Dad lays the turkey on the chopping block and picks up his hatchet. Whack. The hatchet sticks in the frozen turkey flesh. He saws back and forth. Whack. A slice of frozen turkey slides to the ground. He picks it up and waves it at the window. Mom turns her back to him and tells Ted she's on her way.

After Mom leaves for the store, Dad takes over the dinner. It's the principle of the thing. If he gripes about the way she handled Thanksgiving, then he has to prove he can do a better job. He brings in the butchered dirty meat and washes it in the sink with detergent and hot water. He rinses off his hatchet.

Dad: "Just like the old days, right, Mellie? Fellow goes out into the woods and brings home dinner. This isn't so difficult. Cooking just requires some organization and the ability to read. Now get me the bread. I'm going to make real stuffing, the way my mother used to. You don't need to help. Why don't you do some homework, maybe some extra-credit work to pull those grades up. I'll call you when dinner is ready."

I think about studying, but it's a holiday, so I park myself on the living-room couch and watch an old movie instead. I smell smoke twice, wince when glass shatters on the floor, and listen in on the other phone to his conversation with the turkey hotline lady. She says turkey soup is the best part of Thanksgiving anyway. He calls me into the kitchen an hour later, with the fake enthusiasm of a father who has screwed up big-time.

Bones are heaped on the cutting board. A pot of glue boils on the stove. Bits of gray, green, and yellow roll in the burping white paste.

Dad: "It's supposed to be soup."

Me:

Dad: "It tasted a bit watery, so I kept adding thickener. I put in some corn and peas."

Me:

Dad: [pulling wallet from his back pocket] "Call for pizza. I'll get rid of this."

I order double cheese, double mushroom. Dad buries the soup in the back yard next to our dead beagle, Ariel.

WISHBONE

I want to make a memorial for our turkey. Never has a bird been so tortured to provide such a lousy dinner. I dig the bones out of the trash and bring them to art class. Mr. Freeman is thrilled. He tells me to work on the bird but keep thinking tree.

Mr. Freeman: "You are on fire, Melinda, I can see it in your eyes. You are caught up in the meaning, in the subjectivity of the effect of commercialism on this holiday. This is wonderful, wonderful! Be the bird. You are the bird. Sacrifice yourself to abandoned family values and canned yams."

Whatever.

At first, I want to glue the bones together in a heap like firewood (get it?—tree—firewood), but Mr. Freeman sighs. I can do better, he says. I arrange the bones on a black piece of paper and try to draw a turkey around it. I don't need Mr. Freeman to tell me it stinks. By this point, he has thrown himself back into his own painting and has forgotten we exist.

He is working on a huge canvas. It started out bleak—a gutted building along a gray road on a rainy day. He spent a week painting dirty coins on the sidewalk, sweating to get them just right. He painted the faces of school board members peering out the windows of the building, then he put bars on the windows and turned the building into a prison. His canvas is better than TV because you never know what is going to happen next.

I crumple the paper and lay out the bones on the table. Melinda Sordino—Anthropologist. I have unearthed the remains of a hideous sacrifice. The bell rings and I look at Mr. Freeman with puppy-dog eyes. He says he'll call my Spanish teacher with some kind of excuse. I can stay for another class period. When Ivy hears this, she begs permission to stay late, too. She's trying to conquer her fear of clowns. She's constructing some weird sculpture—a mask behind a clown's face. Mr. Freeman says yes to Ivy, too. She waggles her eyebrows at me and grins. By the time I figure out that this might be a good time to say something friendly to her, she is back at work.

I glue the bones to a block of wood, arranging the skeleton like a museum exhibit. I find knives and forks in the odds-'n'-ends bin and glue them so it looks like they are attacking the bones.

I take a step back. It isn't quite done. I rummage in the bin again and find a half-melted palm tree from a Lego set. It'll do. Mr. Freeman hangs on to everything a normal person would throw out: Happy Meal toys, lost playing cards, grocery-store receipts, keys, dolls, a saltshaker, trains . . . how does he know this stuff could be art?

I pop the head off a Barbie doll and set it inside the turkey's body. That feels right. Ivy walks past and looks. She arches her left eyebrow and nods. I wave my hand and Mr. Freeman comes over to inspect. He almost faints with delight.

Mr. Freeman: "Excellent, excellent. What does this say to you?"

Darn. I didn't know there would be a quiz. I clear my throat. I can't get any words out, it is too dry. I try again, with a little cough.

Mr. Freeman: "Sore throat? Don't worry, it's going around. Want me to tell you what I see?"

I nod in relief.

"I see a girl caught in the remains of a holiday gone bad, with her flesh picked off day after day as the carcass dries out. The knife and fork are obviously middle-class sensibilities. The palm tree is a nice touch. A broken dream, perhaps? Plastic honeymoon, deserted island? Oh, if you put it in a slice of pumpkin pie, it could be a desserted island!"

I laugh in spite of myself. I'm getting the hang of this. While Ivy and Mr. Freeman watch, I reach in and pluck out the Barbie head. I set it on top of the bony carcass. There is no place for the palm tree—I toss that aside. I move the knife and fork so they look like legs. I place a piece of tape over Barbie's mouth.

Me: "Do you have any twigs? Little branches? I could use them to make the arms."

Ivy opens her mouth to say something, then closes it again. Mr. Freeman studies my homely project. He doesn't say anything and I'm afraid he's pissed that I took out the palm tree. Ivy tries again. "It's scary," she says. "In a weird way. Not clown scary, um, how do I say this? Like, you don't want to look at it too long. Good job, Mel."

That's not the reaction I was hoping for, but I guess it was positive. She could have turned her nose up, or ignored me, but she didn't. Mr. Freeman taps his chin. He looks way too serious to be an art teacher. He's making me nervous.

64

Mr. Freeman: "This has meaning. Pain."

The bell rings. I leave before he can say more.

PEELED AND CORED

We are studying fruit in biology. Ms. Keen has spent a week teaching us the finer points of stamens and pistils, seedpods and flowers. The earth has frozen, it snows lightly at night, but Ms. Keen is determined to keep Spring alive in her classroom.

The Back Row sleeps until she points out that apple trees need bees to reproduce. "Reproduce" is a trigger word for the Back Row. They have figured out it is related to sex. The lecture on pistils and stamens turns into a big Ha-ha. Ms. Keen has been teaching since the Middle Ages. It would take more than a row full of overheated hypothalamuses (hypothalamii?) to distract her from the day's lesson. She calmly proceeds to the hands-on portion of the lab.

Apples. We each get a Rome or a Cortland or a McIntosh and a plastic knife. We are instructed to dissect. The Back Row holds sword fights. Ms. Keen silently writes their names on the blackboard, along with their current grade. She takes one point off for every minute the sword fight continues. They go from low Bs to very low Cs before they figure out what is going on. They howl.

Back Row: "That's not fair! You can't do that to us! You didn't give us a chance."

She takes off another point. They saw their apples, mutter, mutter, curse, curse, old cow, stupid teacher.

David Petrakis My Lab Partner cuts his apple into eight equal wedges. He doesn't say a word. He is in the middle of a Pre-Med Week. David can't make up his mind between pre-med and pre-law. Ninth grade is a minor inconvenience to him. A zit-cream commercial before the Feature Film of Life.

Applesmell soaks the air. One time when I was little, my parents took me to an orchard. Daddy set me high in an apple tree. It was like falling up into a storybook, yummy and red and leaf and the branch not shaking a bit. Bees bumbled through the air, so stuffed with apple they couldn't be bothered to sting me. The sun warmed my hair, and a wind pushed my mother into my father's arms, and all the apple-picking parents and children smiled for a long, long minute.

That's how biology class smells.

I bite my apple. White teeth red apple hard juice deep bite. David sputters.

David: "You're not supposed to do that! She'll kill you! You're supposed to cut it! Didn't you even listen? You'll lose points!"

Clearly, David missed the apple-tree-sitting requirement of childhood.

I cut the rest of my apple into four fat pieces. My apple has twelve seeds. One of the seeds has split its shell and reaches a white hand upward. An apple tree growing from an apple seed growing in an apple. I show the little plantseed to Ms. Keen. She gives me extra credit. David rolls his eyes. Biology is so cool.

FIRST AMENDMENT, SECOND VERSE

Rebellion is in the air. We only have a week left before Winter Break. Students are getting away with murder and the staff is too worn out to care. I hear rumors of eggnog in the faculty lounge. This revolutionary spirit is even breaking out in social studies class. David Petrakis is fighting back about the freedom-to-speak thing.

I get to class on time. I don't dare use a stolen late pass with Mr. Neck. David takes a seat in the front row and sets a tape recorder on his desk. As Mr. Neck opens his mouth to speak, David presses the Play and Record buttons at the same time, like a pianist hitting an opening chord.

Mr. Neck teaches the class straight. We are galloping toward the Revolutionary War. He writes "No Taxation Without Representation" on the board. Very cool rhyming slogan. Too bad they didn't have bumper stickers back then. The colonists wanted a voice in the British Parliament. No one in power would listen to their complaints. The lecture is going to sound great on the tape. Mr. Neck has prepared notes and everything. His voice is as smooth as a new-poured road. No bumps.

The tape will not be able to pick up the angry gleam in Mr. Neck's eyes, though. He glares at David the whole time he's speaking. If a teacher stared murder at me for forty-eight minutes, I'd turn into a puddle of melted Jell-O. David stares back.

The school office is the best place to go for gossip. I overhear the sound bite about the Petrakises' lawyer while I wait for another lecture from my guidance counselor about not living up to my potential. How does she know what my potential is? Potential for what? When she talks blah blah, I usually count the dots in her ceiling tiles.

The guidance counselor is late today, so I sit invisible in the red plastic chair while the secretary brings a PTA volunteer up to warp speed on the Petrakis thing. David's parents have hired a big, nasty, expensive lawyer. He is threatening to sue the school district and Mr. Neck for everything from incompetence to civil rights violations. David's tape recorder is allowed in class to document "potential future violations." The secretary doesn't sound too upset at the idea that Mr. Neck could get canned. I bet she knows him personally.

David must have mentioned the hairy-eyeball treatment to his lawyer that afternoon because the next day there is a videocamera set up in the back of class. David Petrakis is my hero.

WOMBATS RULE!

I let Heather talk me into going to the Winter Assembly. She hates sitting alone almost as much as I do. The Marthas have not issued an imperial invitation for her to sit with them. She's bummed, but she tries not to show it. In perfect Martha style, she wears a green sweater with a huge Santa face on it, red leggings, and fluffy boots. Too, too perfect. I refuse to wear anything seasonal.

Heather gives me my Christmas present early—bell earrings that chime when I turn my head. This means I'll have to get her something. Maybe I'll go wholesome and buy a friendship necklace. She's the friendship-necklace type. The bells are a great choice. I shake my head all through Principal Principal's speech to drown out his voice. The orchestra plays an unrecognizable tune. Heather says the school board won't let them perform Christmas carols or Hanukkah songs or Kwanza tunes. Instead of multicultural, we have no-cultural.

The high point of the assembly is the announcement of our new name and mascot. Principal Principal reads the vote total: Bees—3. Icebergs—17. Hilltoppers—1. Wombats—32. The other 1,547 votes were write-ins or illegible.

The Merryweather Wombats. Has a nice ring. We are the Wombats, woozy, wicked Wombats! Worried, withdrawn, weepy, weird Wombats. We pass Raven Cheerleader and Amber Cheerleader on the way to my bus. They wrinkle their brows as they struggle to rhyme "wombat." Democracy is a wonderful institution.

WINTER BREAK

School is out and there are two days until Christmas. Mom left a note saying I can put up the tree if I want. I drag the tree out of the basement and stand it in the driveway so I can sweep the dust and cobwebs off it with a broom. We leave the lights on it from year to year. All I have to do is hang the ornaments.

There is something about Christmas that requires a rug rat. Little kids make Christmas fun. I wonder if we could rent one for the holidays. When I was tiny we would buy a real tree and stay up late drinking hot chocolate and finding just the right place for the special decorations. It seems like my parents gave up the magic when I figured out the Santa lie. Maybe I shouldn't have told them I knew where the presents really came from. It broke their hearts.

I bet they'd be divorced by now if I hadn't been born. I'm sure I was a huge disappointment. I'm not pretty or smart or athletic. I'm just like them—an ordinary drone dressed in secrets and lies. I can't believe we have to keep playacting until I graduate. It's a shame we can't just admit that we have failed family living, sell the house, split up the money, and get on with our lives.

Merry Christmas.

I call Heather, but she's shopping. What would Heather do if she were here and the house didn't feel like Christmas? I will pretend to be Heather. I bundle up in geeky snow clothes, wrap a scarf around my head, and plunge into a snowdrift. The back yard is gorgeous. The trees and bushes are all wrapped in ice, reflecting sunlight into something powerful. I just have to make a snow angel.

I tromp to an unmarked piece of snow and let myself fall backward. The scarf falls over my mouth as I wave my wings. The wet wool smells like first grade, walking to school on a cold morning with my milk money jangling in the tips of my mittens. We lived in a different house then, a smaller house. Mom worked at the jewelry counter and was home after school. Dad had a nicer boss and talked all the time about buying a boat. I believed in Santa Claus.

The wind stirs the branches overhead. My heart clangs like a fire bell. The scarf is too tight on my mouth. I pull it off to breathe. The moisture on my skin freezes. I want to make a wish, but I don't know what to wish for. And I have snow up my back.

I break off branches from the holly bushes and a few sprigs of pine and carry them inside. I tie them together with red yarn and set them on the fireplace mantel and the dining-room table. It doesn't look as nice as when the lady on TV did it, but it makes the place smell better. I still wish we could borrow a kid for a few days.

We sleep in till noon on Christmas. I give Mom a black sweater and Dad a CD with sixties hits. They give me a handful of gift certificates, a TV for my room, ice skates, and a sketch pad with charcoal pencils. They say they have noticed me drawing.

I almost tell them right then and there. Tears flood my eyes. They noticed I've been trying to draw. They noticed. I try to swallow the snowball in my throat. This isn't going to be easy. I'm sure they suspect I was at the party. Maybe they even heard about me calling the cops. But I want to tell them everything as we sit there by our plastic Christmas tree while the *Rudolph, the Red-Nosed Reindeer* video plays.

I wipe my eyes. They wait with unsure smiles. The snowball grows larger. When I snuck home that night, they weren't in the house. Both cars were gone. I was supposed to have been at Rachel's all night long—they weren't expecting me, that's for sure. I showered until the hot water was gone, then I crawled in bed and did not sleep. Mom pulled in around 2 a.m., Dad just before sunup. They had not been together. What had they been doing? I thought I knew. How can I talk to them about that night? How can I start?

Rudolph sets out on his ice floe. "I'm independent," he declares. Dad looks at his watch. Mom stuffs the wrapping paper into a garbage bag. They leave the room. I am still sitting on the floor, holding the paper and charcoals. I didn't even say "Thank you."

HARD LABOR

I had two days of freedom before my parents decided I wasn't going to "lounge around the house all vacation." I have to go to work with them. I'm not legally old enough to work, but they don't care. I spend the weekend at Mom's store, dealing with all the merchandise brought back by grumpy people. Did anyone in Syracuse get what they wanted for Christmas? Sure doesn't seem like it. Since I'm underage, Mom sticks me in the basement stockroom. I'm supposed to refold the shirts, sticking them with eleven pins. The other employees watch me like I'm a rat, like my mother has sent me to the basement to spy on them. I fold a few shirts, then kick back and take out a book. They relax. I am one of them. I don't want to be there either.

Mom obviously knows I did squat, but she doesn't say anything in the car. We don't leave until way after dark because she has so much work to do. Sales have sucked—she didn't get anywhere near the goal she set. Layoffs are coming. We stop at a traffic light. Mom closes her eyes. Her skin is a flat gray color, like underwear washed so many times it's about to fall apart. I feel bad that I didn't fold more shirts for her.

The next day they send me to Dad's. He sells some kind of insurance, but I don't know how or why. He sets up a card table for me in his office. My job is to put calendars into envelopes, seal them up, and stick on mailing labels. He sits at his desk and talks to buddies on the phone.

He gets to work with his feet up. He gets to laugh with his friends on the phone. He gets to call out for lunch. I think he deserves to be in the basement folding shirts and helping my mother. I deserve to be watching cable, or taking a nap, or even going to Heather's house. By lunchtime, my stomach boils with anger. Dad's secretary says something nice to me when she drops off my lunch, but I don't answer her. I glare daggers at the back of my father's head. Angry angry angry. I have another million envelopes to close. I run my tongue over the gross gummy envelope flap. The sharp edge of the flap cuts my tongue. I taste my blood. IT's face suddenly pops up in my mind. All the anger whistles out of me like I'm a popped balloon. Dad is really pissed when he sees how many calendars I bled on. He mentions a need for professional help.

I am actually grateful to go back to school.

FOUL

Now that there are two feet of snow on the ground, the fizz-ed teachers let us have class inside. They keep the gym at about forty degrees because "a little cool air never hurt anyone." Easy for them to say, they wear sweatpants.

The first inside sport is basketball. Ms. Connors teaches us how to throw foul shots. I step up to the line, bounce the ball twice, and put it through the net. Ms. Connors tells me to do it again. And again. She keeps bouncing balls my way, and I keep putting them up—swish, swish, swish. Forty-two shots later, my arms wobble and I miss one. By that time, the entire class has gathered around and is watching. Nicole is just about bursting. "You have to join the team!" she shouts.

Ms. Connors: "Meet me back here during activity period. You are Going Places with That Arm."

Me:

It is a sad and downtrodden Ms. Connors who meets me three hours later. She holds my current grades by two fingers: D, C, B–, D, C–, C, A. No basketball team for me, because the A was in art, so my GPA is a whopping 1.7. Ms. Connors did not win a lacrosse scholarship by being demure or hesitant. She times me in wind sprints, then puts me back on the line to shoot.

Ms. Connors: "Try an outside shot bank it off the board have you thought about a tutor nice shot it's those Ds that are killing you try a lay-up that needs work I could maybe do something about the social studies grade but your English teacher is impossible she hates sports do you have a hook shot?"

I just do what I'm told. If I felt like talking, I would explain that she couldn't pay me enough to play on her basketball team. All that running? Sweating? Getting knocked around by genetic mutants? I don't think so. Now, if basketball had a designated foul-shot shooter, maybe I'd consider. The other team fouls you, you get to pay them back. Boom. But that's not the way it works, in basketball or in life.

Ms. Connors looks so eager. I like the sensation of succeeding brilliantly at something—even if it is just thunking in foul shots one after another. I'll let her dream a few more minutes. The boys' varsity team dribbles in. Their record is zero and five. Go Wombats!

Basketball Pole, aka Brendan Keller, the one who contributed to my mashed-potato-and-gravy humiliation on the first day of school, stands under the basket. The other guys run drills and pass in to him. Brendan reaches up a skinny octopus tentacle and casually drops the ball through the hoop. Our boys are unbeatable as long as they are the only team on the floor.

The boys' coach barks something I don't understand and the team lines up behind Basketball Pole for free-throw practice. He dribbles, bounce, two, three. He shoots. Brick. Bounce, two, three . . . Brick. Brick. Brick. Can't sink a shot from the line to save his skinny neck.

Ms. Connors talks to the boys' coach while I watch the rest of the team hit a sorry thirty percent. Then she blows her whistle and waves me over. The boys clear out of the way and I take my place on the line. "Show 'em," commands Ms. Connors. Trained seal me, bounce, bounce, up, swish; again, and again, and again, until the guys stop bouncing and everyone is watching. Ms. Connors and Basketball Coach talk serious frown talk arms on hips, biceps flexing. The boys stare at me—visitor from the Planet Foul Shot. Who is this girl?

Ms. Connors punches Coach in the arm. Coach punches Ms. Connors in the arm. They offer me a deal. If I volunteer to teach the Basketball Pole how to swish a foul shot, I will get an automatic A in gym. I shrug my shoulders and they grin. I couldn't say no. I couldn't say anything. I just won't show up.

COLORING OUTSIDE THE LINES

Our art room is blooming like a museum full of O'Keeffes, van Goghs, and that French guy who painted flowers with tiny dots. Mr. Freeman is the Vogue Teacher of the Moment. There are rumors that he'll be the Teacher of the Year in the yearbook.

His room is Cool Central. He keeps the radio on. We are allowed to eat as long as we work. He bounced a couple of slackers who confused freedom with no rules, so the rest of us don't make waves. It is too much fun to give up. The room is full of painters, sculptors, and sketchers during activity period, and some kids stay there until the late late buses are ready to roll.

Mr. Freeman's painting is coming along great. Some newspaper guy heard about it and wrote an article. The article claimed Mr. Freeman is a gifted genius who has devoted his life to education. A color picture of the work-in-progress accompanied the article. Someone said a few school board members recognized themselves. I bet they sue him.

I wish Mr. Freeman would put a tree in his masterpiece. I can't figure out how to make mine look real. I have already ruined six linoleum blocks. I can see it in my head: a strong old oak tree with a wide scarred trunk and thousands of leaves reaching to the sun. There's a tree in front of my house just like it. I can feel the wind blow and hear the mockingbird whistling on the way back to her nest. But when I try to carve it, it looks like a dead tree, toothpicks, a child's drawing. I can't bring it to life. I'd love to give it up. Quit. But I can't think of anything else to do, so I keep chipping away at it.

Principal Principal stormed in yesterday, smelling pleasure. His mustache moved up and down, a radar sweep for all things unruly. An unseen hand turned off the radio as he crossed the threshold, and bags of potato chips vanished, leaving the faint scent of salt to mix with vermilion oil paint and wet clay.

He scanned the room for merriment. Found only bowed heads, graceful pencils, dipping brushes. Mr. Freeman touched up the dark roots on the head of a lady school board member and asked if Principal Principal needed help. Principal Principal stalked out of the room in the direction of the Human Waste's smoking haven.

Maybe I'll be an artist if I grow up.

POSTER CHILD

Heather left a note in my locker, begging me to go to her house after school. She's in trouble. She is not meeting Martha standards. She sobs out the story in her room. I listen and pick lint balls off my sweater.

The Marthas held a craft meeting to make Valentine's pillows for little kids who are in the hospital. Meg 'n' Emily sewed three sides of the pillows, while the others stuffed, stitched, and glued on hearts and teddy bears. Heather was in charge of hearts. She was all flustered because a few Marthas didn't like her outfit. They yelled at her for gluing hearts crooked. Then the top of her glue bottle came off and completely ruined a pillow.

At this point in the story, she throws a doll across her room. I move the nail polish out of her reach.

Meg demoted Heather to pillow stuffing. Once the pillow production line was again rolling smoothly, the meeting began. Topic: the Canned Food Drive. The Senior Marthas are in charge of delivering the food to the needy (with a newspaper photographer present) and meeting with the principal to coordinate whatever needs coordinating.

I zone out. She talks about who's in charge of classroom captains and who's in charge of publicity and I don't know what all. I don't come back to earth until Heather says, "I knew you wouldn't mind, Mel."

Me: "What?"

Heather: "I knew you wouldn't mind helping. I think Emily did it on purpose. She doesn't like me. I was going to ask you to help, then say I did it by myself, but that would have been lying, and besides they would have stuck me with all the poster work for the rest of the year. So I said I have a friend who is really artistic and community-oriented and could she help with the posters?"

Me: "Who?"

Heather: [laughing now, but I still hold on to the nail polish] "You, silly. You draw better than me and you have plenty of time. Please say you'll do it! Maybe they'll ask you to join too, once they see how talented you are! Please, please, whipped cream, chopped nuts and cherry on top please! If I screw this up, I know they'll blacklist me and then I'll never be part of any of the good groups."

How could I say no?

DEAD FROGS

Our biology class has graduated from fruit to frogs. We were scheduled to do the frog unit in April, but the frog company delivered our victims on January 14. Pickled frogs have a way of disappearing from the storage closet, so today Ms. Keen armed us with knives and told us not to gag.

David Petrakis My Lab Partner is thrilled—anatomy at last. There are lists to memorize. The hopping bone's connected to the jumping bone, the ribbet bone's connected to the fly-catching bone. He seriously talks about wearing one of those doctor masks over his face while we "operate." He thinks it would be good practice.

The room does not smell like apple. It smells like frog juice, a cross between a nursing home and potato salad. The Back Row pays attention. Cutting dead frogs is cool.

Our frog lies on her back. Waiting for a prince to come and princessify her with a smooch? I stand over her with my knife. Ms. Keen's voice fades to a mosquito whine. My throat closes off. It is hard to breathe. I put out my hand to steady myself against the table. David pins her froggy hands to the dissection tray. He spreads her froggy legs and pins her froggy feet. I have to slice open her belly. She doesn't say a word. She is already dead. A scream starts in my gut—I can feel the cut, smell the dirt, leaves in my hair.

I don't remember passing out. David says I hit my head on the edge of the table on my way down. The nurse calls my mom because I need stitches. The doctor stares into the back of my eyes with a bright light. Can she read the thoughts hidden there? If she can, what will she do? Call the cops? Send me to the nuthouse? Do I want her to? I just want to sleep. The whole point of not talking about it, of silencing the memory, is to make it go away. It won't. I'll need brain surgery to cut it out of my head. Maybe I should wait until David Petrakis is a doctor, let him do it.

MODEL CITIZEN

Heather has landed a modeling job at a department store in the mall. She says she was buying socks with her mother the week after her braces came off and some lady asked if she modeled. I suspect the fact that her dad works for the mall management company had something to do with it.

The modeling gig is paying off in major Martha points. They all want to be Heather's New Best Friend. But she asks me to go with her for the bathing suit shoot. I think she's afraid to screw up in front of them. Heather's mother drives us. She asks if I want to be a model. Heather says I am too shy. I look at her mother's eyes watching me in the rearview mirror and hide my mouth with my fingers. The scabs on my lips are especially gross in that little rectangle mirror.

Of course I want to be a model. I want to paint my eyelids gold. I saw that on a magazine cover and it looked amazing— turned the model into a sexy alien that everyone would look at but nobody dared touch.

I like cheeseburgers too much to be a model. Heather has stopped eating and complains about fluid retention. She should worry more about brain retention, the way she's dieting away her gray matter. At last check, she was wearing a size one and a half, and she just *has* to get down to a size one.

The photo shoot is in a building cold enough to store ice. Heather looks like our Thanksgiving turkey wearing a blue bikini. Her goose bumps are bigger than her boobs. I'm shivering, and I'm wearing my ski jacket and a wool sweater. The photographer turns up the radio and starts bossing the girls around. Heather totally gets into it. She throws her head back, stares at the camera, flashes her teeth. The photographer keeps saying, "Sexy, sexy, very cute. Look this way. Sexy, think beach, think boys." It creeps me out. Heather sneezes in the middle of a group pose and her mother runs in with tissues. It must be catching. My throat is killing me. I want a nap.

I don't buy the gold eyeshadow, but I do pick up a bottle of Black Death nail polish. It's gloomy, with squiggly lines of red in it. My nails are bitten to the bleeding point, so it will look natural. I need to get a shirt that matches. Something in a tubercular gray.

DEATH BY ALGEBRA

Mr. Stetman won't give up. He is determined to prove once and for all that algebra is something we will use the rest of our lives. If he succeeds, I think they should give him the Teacher of the Century Award and a two-week vacation in Hawaii, all expenses paid.

He comes to class each day with a new Real-Life Application. It is sweet that he cares enough about algebra and his students to want to bring them together. He's like a grandfather who wants to fix up two young kids that he just knows would make a great couple. Only the kids have nothing in common and they hate each other.

Today's Application has something to do with buying guppies at the pet store, and calculating how many guppies you could breed if you wanted to go into the guppie business. Once the guppies turn into x's and y's, my contacts fog. Class ends in a debate between the animal-rights activists, who say it is immoral to own fish, and the red-blooded capitalists, who know lots of better ways to make money than investing in fish that eat their young. I watch the snow falling outside.

WORD WORK

Hairwoman is torturing us with essays. Do English teachers spend their vacations dreaming up these things?

The first essay this semester was a dud: "Why America Is Great" in five hundred words. She gave us three weeks. Only Tiffany Wilson turned it in on time. But the assignment was not a complete failure—Hairwoman runs the drama club and she recruited several new members based on their performances as to why they needed an extension.

She has a warped sense of humor as well as a demented beautician. The next essay was supposed to be fictional: "The Best

Lost Homework Excuse Ever" in five hundred words. We had one night. No one was late.

But now Hairwoman is on a roll. "How I Would Change High School," "Lower the Driving Age to 14," "The Perfect Job." Her topics are fun, but she keeps cranking them out, one after the next. First she broke our spirits by overwhelming us with work we couldn't really complain about because the topics are the kind of things we talk about all the time. Recently she's started sneaking grammar (shudder) into the classroom. One day we worked on verb tenses: "I surf the Net, I surfed the Net, I was surfing the Net." Then, lively adjectives. Does it sound better to say "Nicole's old lacrosse stick hit me on the head" or "Nicole's barf-yellow, gnarled, bloodstained lacrosse stick hit me on the head"? She even tried to teach us the difference between active voice—"I snarfed the Oreos"—and passive voice—"The Oreos got snarfed."

Words are hard work. I hope they send Hairwoman to a conference or something. I'm ready to help pay for a sub.

NAMING THE MONSTER

I work on Heather's posters for two weeks. I try to draw them in the art room, but too many people watch me. It is quiet in my closet, and the markers smell good. I could stay here forever. BRING A CAN, SAVE A LIFE. Heather told me to be direct. It is the only way to get what we want. I draw posters of basketball players shooting cans through a hoop. They demonstrate very good form.

Heather has another modeling job. Tennis clothes, I think. She asks me to hang the posters for her. I actually don't mind. It's nice having kids see me do something good. Might help my reputation. I'm hanging a poster outside the metal-shop room when IT creeps up. Little flecks of metal slice through my veins. IT whispers to me.

"Freshmeat." That's what IT whispers.

IT found me again. I thought I could ignore IT. There are four hundred other freshmen in here, two hundred female. Plus all the other grades. But he whispers to me.

I can smell him over the noise of the metal shop and I drop my poster and the masking tape and I want to throw up and I can smell him and I run and he remembers and he knows. He whispers in my ear.

I lie to Heather about the masking tape and say I put it back in the supply box.

RENT ROUND 3

My guidance counselor calls Mom at the store to pave the way for my report card. Must remember to send her a thank-you note. By the time we eat dinner, the Battle is roaring at full pitch. Grades, blah, blah, blah, Attitude, blah, blah, blah, Help around the house, blah, blah, blah, Not a kid anymore, blah, blah, blah.

I watch the Eruptions. Mount Dad, long dormant, now considered armed and dangerous. Mount Saint Mom, oozing lava, spitting flame. Warn the villagers to run into the sea. Behind my eyes I conjugate irregular Spanish verbs.

A minor blizzard blows outside. The weather lady says it's a lake-effect storm—the wind from Canada sucks up water from Lake Ontario, runs it through the freeze machine, and dumps it on Syracuse. I can feel the wind fighting to break through our storm windows. I want the snow to bury our house.

They keep asking questions like "What is wrong with you?" and "Do you think this is cute?" How can I answer? I don't have to. They don't want to hear anything I have to say. They ground me until the Second Coming. I have to come straight home after school unless Mom arranges for me to meet with a teacher. I can't go to Heather's. They are going to disconnect the cable. (Don't think they'll follow through on that one.)

I do my homework and show it to them like a good little girl. When they send me to bed, I write a runaway note and leave it on my desk. Mom finds me sleeping in my bedroom closet. She hands me a pillow and closes the door again. No more blah-blahs.

I open up a paper clip and scratch it across the inside of my left wrist. Pitiful. If a suicide attempt is a cry for help, then what is this? A whimper, a peep? I draw little windowcracks of blood, etching line after line until it stops hurting. It looks like I arm-wrestled a rosebush.

Mom sees the wrist at breakfast.

Mom: "I don't have time for this, Melinda."

Me:

She says suicide is for cowards. This is an uglynasty Momside. She bought a book about it. Tough love. Sour sugar. Barbed velvet. Silent talk. She leaves the book on the back of the toilet to educate me. She has figured out that I don't say too much. It bugs her.

CAN IT

Lunch with Heather starts cold. Since winter break, she has been sitting at the fringe of the Martha table and I eat on the other side of her. I can tell something is up as soon as I walk in. All the Marthas are wearing matching outfits: navy corduroy miniskirts, striped tops, and clear plastic purses. They must have gone shopping together. Heather doesn't match. They hadn't invited her.

She is too cool to be nervous about this. I am nervous for her. I take an enormous bite of my PBJ and try not to choke. They wait until she has a mouthful of cottage cheese. Siobhan puts a can of beets on the table.

Siobhan: "What's this?"

Heather: [swallowing] "It's a can of beets."

Siobhan: "No duh. But we found an entire bag of beets in the collection closet. They must have come from you."

Heather: "A neighbor gave them to me. They're beets. People eat them. What's the problem?"

The rest of the Marthas sigh on cue. Apparently, beets are Not Good Enough. Real Marthas only collect food that they like to eat, like cranberry sauce, dolphin-safe tuna, or baby peas. I can see Heather dig her nails into her palms under the table. The peanut butter molds to the roof of my mouth like a retainer.

Siobhan: "That's not all. Your numbers are abysmal."

Heather: "What numbers?"

Siobhan: "Your can quota. You aren't carrying your weight. You aren't contributing."

Heather: "We've only been doing this for a week. I know I'll get more."

Emily: "It's not just the can quota. Your posters are ridiculous—my little brother could have done a better job. It's no wonder no one wants to help us. You've turned this project into a joke."

Emily slides her tray across to Heather. Heather gets up without a word and clears it away. Traitor. She isn't going to stick up for my posters. The peanut butter in my mouth hardens.

Siobhan pokes Emily and looks at the door.

Siobhan: "It's him. Andy Evans just walked in. I think he's looking for you, Em."

I turn around. They are talking about IT. Andy. Andy Evans. Short stabby name. Andy Evans, who strolls in carrying a take-out bag from Taco Bell. He offers the cafeteria monitor a burrito. Emily and Siobhan giggle. Heather returns, her smile back in place, and asks if Andy is as bad as everyone says. Emily blushes the color of canned beets.

Siobhan: "It's just a rumor."

Emily: "Fact—he's gorgeous. Fact—he's rich. Fact—he's just the itsiest bit dangerous and he called me last night."

Siobhan: "Rumor—he sleeps with anything."

The peanut butter locks my jaws closed.

Emily: "I don't believe it. Rumors are spread by jealous people. Hi, Andy. Did you bring enough lunch for everyone?"

It feels like the Prince of Darkness has swept his cloak over the table. The lights dim. I shiver. Andy stands behind me to flirt with Emily. I lean into the table to stay as far away from him as I can. The table saws me in half. Emily's mouth moves, the fluorescent lights glittering on her teeth. The other girls scooch toward Emily to soak up her Attractiveness Rays. Andy must be talking too, I can feel deep vibrations in my backbone, like a thudding speaker. I can't hear the words.

He twirls my ponytail in his fingers. Emily's eyes narrow. I mumble something idiotic and run for the bathroom. I heave lunch into the toilet, then wash my face with the ice water that comes out of the Hot faucet. Heather does not come looking for me.

DARK ART

The cement-slab sky hangs inches above our heads. Which direction is east? It has been so long since I've seen the sun, I can't remember. Turtlenecks creep out of bottom drawers. Turtle faces pull back into winter clothes. We won't see some kids until spring.

Mr. Freeman is in trouble. Big-time. He gave up paperwork when the school board Xed out his supply budget. They have caught up with him. Teachers just handed in the second-marking-period grades and Mr. Freeman gave out 210 As. Someone smelled a rat. Probably the office secretary.

I wonder if they called him down to Principal Principal's office and put this on his Permanent Record. He has stopped working on his canvas, the painting we all thought was going to be this awesome, earth-shattering piece of art that would be auctioned for a million dollars. The art room is cold, Mr. Freeman's face a shade of gray-purple. If he wasn't so depressed, I'd ask him what the name of that color is. He just sits on his stool, a blue broken cricket husk.

No one talks to him. We blow on our fingers to warm them up and sculpt or draw or paint or sketch, or, in my case, carve. I start a new linoleum block. My last tree looked like it had died from some fungal infection—not the effect I wanted at all. The cold makes the linoleum stiffer than usual. I dig the chisel into the block and push, trying to follow the line of a tree trunk.

I follow the line of my thumb instead and gash myself. I swear and stick my thumb in my mouth. Everybody looks at me, so I take it out again. Mr. Freeman hurries over with a box of Kleenex. It isn't a deep cut, and I shake my head when he asks if I want to go to the nurse's office. He washes my chisel off in the sink and puts bleach on it. Some sort of AIDS regulation. When it is germ-free and dry, he carries it back toward my table, but stops in front of his canvas. He hasn't finished painting. The bottom right corner is empty. The prisoners' faces are menacing—you can't take your eyes off them. I wouldn't want a painting like that hanging over my couch. It looks like it might come alive at night.

Mr. Freeman steps back, as if he has just seen something new in his own picture. He slices the canvas with my chisel, ruining it with a long, ripping sound that makes the entire class gasp.

MY REPORT CARD

Attitude	D	Social Studies	D	Spanish	C–	Art	A
Lunch	C	Biology	B	Algebra	C–		
Clothes	C–	English	C–	Gym	C–		

THIRD MARKING PERIOD

DEATH OF THE WOMBAT

The Wombat is dead. No assembly, no vote. Principal Principal made an announcement this morning. He said hornets better represent the Merryweather spirit than foreign marsupials, plus the Wombat mascot costume was going to suck money from the prom committee's budget. We are the Hornets and that is final.

The seniors support this decision totally. They wouldn't be able to hold up their heads if the prom had to be moved from the Holiday Inn Ballroom to the gym. That would be so elementary-school.

Our cheerleaders are working on annoying chants that end in lots of buzzing. I think this is a mistake. I have visions of opposing teams making enormous flyswatters and giant cans of insecticide out of papier-mâché to humiliate us during halftime programs.

I'm allergic to hornets. One sting and my skin bubbles with hives and my throat closes up.

COLD WEATHER AND BUSES

I miss the bus because I couldn't believe how dark it was when my alarm clock went off. I need a clock that will turn on a

300-watt bulb when it's time to get up. Either that or a rooster.

When I realize how late it is, I decide not to rush. Why bother? Mom comes downstairs and I'm reading the funnies and eating oatmeal.

Mom: "You missed the bus again."

I nod.

Mom: "You expect me to drive you again."

Another nod.

Mom: "You'll need boots. It's a long walk and it snowed again last night. I'm already late."

That is unexpected, but not harsh. The walk isn't that bad— it's not like she made me hike ten miles through a snowstorm uphill in both directions or anything. The streets are quiet and pretty. The snow covers yesterday's slush and settles on the rooftops like powdered sugar on a gingerbread town.

By the time I get to Fayette's, the town bakery, I'm hungry again. Fayette's makes wicked good jelly doughnuts and I have lunch money in my pocket. I decide to buy two dough-nuts and call it brunch.

I cross the parking lot and IT comes out the door. Andy Evans with a raspberry-dripping jelly doughnut in one hand and a cup of coffee in the other. I stop on a frozen puddle. Maybe he

96

won't notice me if I stand still. That's how rabbits survive; they freeze in the presence of predators.

He sets the coffee on top of his car and fumbles in his pocket for the keys. Very, very adult, this coffee/car-keys/cut-school guy. He drops the keys and swears. He isn't going to notice me. I'm not here—he can't see me standing here in my purple marshmallow jacket.

But of course my luck with this guy sucks. So he turns his head and sees me. And wolfsmiles, showing oh granny what big teeth you have.

He steps toward me, holding out the doughnut. "Want a bite?" he asks.

BunnyRabbit bolts, leaving fast tracks in the snow. Getaway getaway getaway. Why didn't I run like this before when I was a one-piece talking girl?

Running makes me feel like I am eleven years old and fast. I burn a strip up the sidewalk, melting snow and ice three feet on either side. When I stop, a brand-new thought explodes in my head:

Why go to school?

ESCAPE

The first hour of blowing off school is great. No one to tell me what to do, what to read, what to say. It's like living in an

MTV video—not with the stupid costumes, but wearing that butt-strutting, I-do-what-I-want additood.

I wander down Main Street. Beauty parlor, 7–Eleven, bank, card store. The rotating bank sign says it is 22 degrees. I wander up the other side. Appliance store, hardware store, parking lot, grocery store. My insides are cold from breathing in frozen air. I can feel the hairs in my nose crackle. My strut slows to a foot-dragging schlump. I even think about trudging uphill to school. At least it's heated.

I bet kids in Arizona enjoy playing hooky more than kids trapped in Central New York. No slush. No yellow snow.

I'm saved by a Centro bus. It coughs and rumbles and spits out two old women in front of the grocery store. I climb on. Destination: The Mall.

You never think about the mall being closed. It's always supposed to be there, like milk in the refrigerator or God. But it is just opening when I get off the bus. Store managers juggle key rings and extra-large coffees, then the cage gates fly up in the air. Lights wink on, the fountains jump, music plays behind the giant ferns, and the mall is open.

White-haired grandmas and grandpops powerwalk squeak-squeak, going so fast they don't even look at the window displays. I hunt spring fashions—nothing that fit last year fits now. How can I shop with Mom if I don't want to talk to her? She might love it—no arguing that way. But then I'd have to wear the clothes she picked out. Conundrum—a three-point vocab word.

I sit by the central elevator, where they set up Santa's Workshop after Halloween. The air smells like french fries and floor cleaner. The sun through the skylight is summer hot and I shed layers—jacket, hat, mittens, sweater. I lose seven pounds in half a minute, feel like I could float up alongside the elevator. Tiny brown birds sing above me. No one knows how they got in, but they live in the mall and sing pretty. I lie on the bench and watch the birds weave through the warm air until the sun burns so bright I'm afraid it will make holes in my eyeballs.

I should probably tell someone, just tell someone. Get it over with. Let it out, blurt it out.

I want to be in fifth grade again. Now, *that* is a deep dark secret, almost as big as the other one. Fifth grade was easy—old enough to play outside without Mom, too young to go off the block. The perfect leash length.

A rent-a-cop strolls by. He studies the wax women in the Sears window, then strolls back the other way. He doesn't even bother with a fake smile, or an "Are you lost?" I'm not in fifth grade. He starts back for a third pass, his finger on his radio. Will he turn me in? Time to find that bus stop.

I spend the rest of the day waiting for it to be 2:48, so it's not all that different from school. I figure I learned a good lesson, and set my alarm clock early for the next day. I wake up on time for four days in a row, get on the bus four days in a row, ride home after school. I want to scream. I think I'll need to take a day off every once in a while.

CODE BREAKING

Hairwoman has been buying new earrings. One pair hangs all the way down to her shoulders. Another has bells in them like the pair Heather gave me at Christmas. I guess I can't wear mine anymore. There should be a law.

It's Nathaniel Hawthorne Month in English. Poor Nathaniel. Does he know what they've done to him? We are reading *The Scarlet Letter* one sentence at a time, tearing it up and chewing on its bones.

It's all about SYMBOLISM, says Hairwoman. Every word chosen by Nathaniel, every comma, every paragraph break— these were all done on purpose. To get a decent grade in her class, we have to figure out what he was really trying to say. Why couldn't he just say what he meant? Would they pin scarlet letters on his chest? B for blunt, S for straightforward?

I can't whine too much. Some of it is fun. It's like a code, breaking into his head and finding the key to his secrets. Like the whole guilt thing. Of course you know the minister feels guilty and Hester feels guilty, but Nathaniel wants us to know this is a big deal. If he kept repeating, "She felt guilty, she felt guilty, she felt guilty," it would be a boring book and no one would buy it. So he planted SYMBOLS, like the weather, and the whole light and dark thing, to show us how poor Hester feels.

I wonder if Hester tried to say no. She's kind of quiet. We would get along. I can see us, living in the woods, her wearing that A, me with an S maybe, S for silent, for stupid, for scared. S for silly. For shame.

So the code-breaking part was fun for the first lesson, but a little of it goes a long way. Hairwoman is hammering it to death.

Hairwoman: "The description of the house with bits of glass embedded in the walls—what does it mean?"

Utter silence from the class. A fly left over from fall buzzes against the cold window. A locker slams in the hall. Hairwoman answers her own question.

"Think of what that would look like, a wall with glass embedded in it. It would . . . reflect? Sparkle? Shine on sunny days maybe. Come on, people, I shouldn't have to do this by myself. Glass in the wall. We use that on top of prison walls nowadays. Hawthorne is showing us that the house is a prison, or a dangerous place maybe. It is hurtful. Now, I asked you to find some examples of the use of color. Who can list a few pages where color is described?"

The fly buzzes a farewell buzz and dies.

Rachel/Rachelle, my ex–best friend: "Who cares what the color means? How do you know what he meant to say? I mean, did he leave another book called 'Symbolism in My Books'? If he didn't, then you could just be making all of this up. Does anyone really think this guy sat down and stuck all kinds of hidden meanings into his story? It's just a story."

Hairwoman: "This is Hawthorne, one of the greatest American novelists! He didn't do anything by accident—he was a genius."

Rachel/Rachelle: "I thought we were supposed to have opinions here. My opinion is that it's kind of hard to read, but the part about how Hester gets in trouble and the preacher guy almost gets away with it, well, that's a good story. But I think you are making all this symbolism stuff up. I don't believe any of it."

Hairwoman: "Do you tell your math teacher you don't believe that three times four equals twelve? Well, Hawthorne's symbolism is just like multiplication—once you figure it out, it's as clear as day."

The bell rings. Hairwoman blocks the door to give out our assignment. A five-hundred-word essay on symbolism, how to find hidden meanings in Hawthorne. The whole class yells at Rachel/Rachelle in the hall.

That's what you get for speaking up.

STUNTED

Mr. Freeman has found a way around the authorities again. He painted the names of all his students on one wall of the classroom, then made a column for each week left of school. Each week he evaluates our progress and makes a note on the wall. He calls it a necessary compromise.

Next to my name he's painted a question mark. My tree is frozen. A kindergartner could carve a better tree. I've stopped counting the linoleum blocks I ruined. Mr. Freeman has reserved the rest of them for me. Good thing, too. I am dying to try a different subject, something easy like designing an entire city or copying the *Mona Lisa*, but he won't budge. He suggested I try a different medium, so I used purple finger paints. The paint cooled my hands, but did nothing for my tree. Trees.

On a shelf I find a book of landscapes filled with illustrations of every stinking tree that grows: sycamore, linden, aspen, willow, fir, tulip poplar, chestnut, elm, spruce, pine. Their bark, flowers, limbs, needles, nuts. I feel like a regular forester, but I can't do what I'm supposed to. The last time Mr. Freeman had anything good to say to me was when I made that stupid turkey-bone thing.

Mr. Freeman is having his own problems. He mostly sits on his stool and stares at a new canvas. It is painted one color, so blue it's almost black. No light comes out of it or goes in, no shadows without light. Ivy asks him what it is. Mr. Freeman snaps out of his funk and looks at her like he just realized the room was full of students.

Mr. Freeman: "It is Venice at night, the color of an accountant's soul, a love rejected. I grew mold on an orange this color when I lived in Boston. It's the blood of imbeciles. Confusion. Tenure. The inside of a lock, the taste of iron. Despair. A city with the streetlights shot out. Smoker's lung. The hair of a small girl who grows up hopeless. The heart of a school board director . . ."

He is warming up for a full-fledged rant when the bell rings. Some teachers rumorwhisper he's having a breakdown. I think he's the sanest person I know.

LUNCH DOOM

Nothing good ever happens at lunch. The cafeteria is a giant sound stage where they film daily segments of Teenage Humiliation Rituals. And it smells gross.

I sit with Heather, as usual, but we are off by ourselves in a corner by the courtyard, not near the Marthas. Heather sits so her back is to the rest of the cafeteria. She can watch the wind shift the drifts of snow trapped in the courtyard behind me. I can feel the wind seep through the glass and penetrate my shirt.

I am not listening too closely as Heather ahems her way to what is on her mind. The noise of four hundred mouths moving, consuming, pulls me away from her. The background pulsing of the dishwashers, the squeal of announcements that no one hears—it is a vespiary, the Hornet haven. I am a small ant crouched by the entrance, with the winter wind at my back. I smother my green beans with mashed potatoes.

Heather nibbles through her jicama and whole-grain roll, and blows me off while she eats her baby carrots.

Heather: "This is really awkward. I mean, how do you say something like this? No matter what . . . no, I don't want to say that. I mean, we kind of paired up at the beginning of the year when I was new and didn't know anyone and that was really, really sweet of you, but I think it's time for us both to admit that we . . . just . . . are . . . very . . . different."

She studies her no-fat yogurt. I try to think of something bitchy, something wicked and cruel. I can't.

Me: "You mean we're not friends anymore?"

Heather: [smiling with her mouth but not her eyes] "We were never really, really friends, were we? I mean, it's not like I ever slept over at your house or anything. We like to do different things. I have my modeling, and I like to shop . . ."

Me: "I like to shop."

Heather: "You don't like anything. You are the most depressed person I've ever met, and excuse me for saying this, but you are no fun to be around and I think you need professional help."

Up until this very instant, I had never seriously thought of Heather as my one true friend in the world. But now I am desperate to be her pal, her buddy, to giggle with her, to gossip with her. I want her to paint my toenails.

Me: "I was the only person who talked to you on the first day of school, and now you're blowing me off because I'm a little depressed? Isn't that what friends are for, to help each other out in bad times?"

Heather: "I knew you would take this the wrong way. You are just so weird sometimes."

I squint at the wall of hearts on the other side of the room. Lovers can spend five dollars to get a red or pink heart with their initials on it mounted on the wall for Valentine's Day. It looks so out of place, those red splotches on blue. The jocks—excuse me—the student athletes, sit in front of the hearts to judge the new romances. Poor Heather. There are no Hallmark cards for breaking up with friends.

I know what she's thinking. She has a choice: she can hang out with me and get the reputation of being a creepy weirdo who might show up with a gun someday, or she can be a Martha—one of the girls who get good grades, do nice things, and ski well. Which would I choose?

Heather: "When you get through this Life Sucks phase, I'm sure lots of people will want to be your friend. But you just can't cut classes or not show up to school. What's next—hanging out with the dopers?"

Me: "Is this the part where you try to be nice to me?"

Heather: "You have a reputation."

Me: "For what?"

Heather: "Look, you can't eat lunch with me anymore. I'm sorry. Oh, and don't eat those potato chips. They'll make you break out."

She neatly wraps her trash into a wax-paper ball and deposits it in the garbage can. Then she walks to the Martha table. Her friends scooch down to make room for her. They swallow her whole and she never looks back at me. Not once.

CONJUGATE THIS

I cut class, you cut class, he, she, it cuts class. We cut class, they cut class. We all cut class. I cannot say this in Spanish, because I did not go to Spanish today. *Gracias a dios. Hasta luego.*

CUTTING OUT HEARTS

When we get off the bus on Valentine's Day, a girl with white-blond hair bursts into tears. "I Love You, Anjela!" is spray-painted into the snowbank along the parking lot. I don't know if Angela is crying because she is happy or because her heart's desire can't spell. Her honey is waiting with a red rose. They kiss right there in front of everybody. Happy Valentine's Day.

It's caught me by surprise. Valentine Day's was a big hairy deal in elementary school because you had to give cards to everyone in your class, even the kid who made you step in dog poop. Then the class mom brought in pink frosted cupcakes and we traded those little candy hearts that said "Hot Baby!" and "Be Mine!"

The holiday went underground in middle school. No parties. No shoe boxes with red cutout hearts for your drugstore valentines. To tell someone you liked them, you had to use layers and layers of friends, as in "Janet told me to tell you that Steven told me that Dougie said Carom was talking to April and she hinted that Sara's brother Mark has a friend named Tony who might like you. What are you going to do?"

It is easier to floss with barbed wire than admit you like someone in middle school.

I go with the flow toward my locker. We are all dressed in down jackets and vests, so we collide and roll like bumper cars at the state fair. I notice envelopes taped to some lockers but don't really think about it until I find one on mine. It says "Melinda." It has to be a joke. Someone put it there to make me look stupid. I peer over my left shoulder, then my right, for groups of evil kids pointing at me. All I see are the backs of heads.

What if it is real? What if it's from a boy? My heart stops, then stutters and pumps again. No, not Andy. His style is definitely not romantic. Maybe David Petrakis My Lab Partner. He watches me when he thinks I can't see him, afraid I'm going to break lab equipment or faint again. Sometimes he smiles at me, an anxious smile, the kind you use on a dog that might bite. All I have to do is open the envelope. I can't stand it. I walk past my locker and go straight to biology.

Ms. Keen decided it would be cute to review birds and bees in honor of Valentine's Day. Nothing practical, of course, no information about why hormones can make you crazy, or why your face only breaks out at the worst time, or how to tell if somebody really gave you a Valentine's card on your locker. No, she really teaches us about the birds and the bees. Notes of love and betrayal are passed hand over hand as if the lab tables were lanes on Cupid's Highway. Ms. Keen draws a picture of an egg with a baby chick inside it.

David Petrakis is fighting to stay awake. Does he like me? I make him nervous. He thinks I'm going to ruin his grade. But maybe I'm growing on him. Do I want him to like me? I chew my thumbnail. No. I just want anyone to like me. I want a note with a heart on it. I pull the edge of my thumbnail back too far and it bleeds. I squeeze my thumb so the blood gathers in a perfect sphere before it collapses and slides toward the palm of my hand. David hands me a tissue. I press it into the cut. The white cells of paper dissolve as the red floods them. It doesn't hurt. Nothing hurts except the small smiles and blushes that flash across the room like tiny sparrows.

I open my notebook and write a note to David: "Thanks!" I slide the notebook over to him. He swallows hard, his Adam's apple bouncing to the bottom of his neck and back up again. He writes back: "You are welcome." Now what? I squeeze the tissue harder on my thumb to concentrate. Ms. Keen's baby bird hatches on the board. I draw a picture of Ms. Keen as a robin. David smiles. He draws a branch under her feet and slides the notebook back to me. I try to connect the branch to a tree. It looks pretty good, better than anything I have drawn so far in art. The bell rings, and David's hand brushes against mine as he picks up his books. I bolt from my seat. I'm afraid to look at him. What if he thinks I already opened his card and I hate his guts, which was why I didn't say anything? But I can't say anything because the card could be a joke, or from some other silent watcher who blends in with the blur of lockers and doors.

My locker. The card is still there, a white patch of hope with my name on it. I tear it off and open it. Something falls to my feet. The card has a picture of two cutesy teddy bears sharing a pot of honey. I open it. "Thanks for understanding. You're the sweetest!" It is signed with a purple pen. "Good Luck!!! Heather."

I bend down to find what dropped from the card. It was the friendship necklace I had given Heather in a fit of insanity around Christmas. Stupid stupid stupid. How stupid could I be? I hear a cracking inside me, my ribs are collapsing in on my lungs, which is why I can't breathe. I stumble down the hall, down another hall, down another hall, till I find my very own door and slip inside and throw the lock, not even bothering to turn on the lights, just falling falling a mile downhill to the bottom of my brown chair, where I can sink my teeth into the soft white skin of my wrist and cry like the baby I am. I rock, thumping my head against the cinder-block wall. A half-forgotten holiday has unveiled every knife that sticks inside me, every cut. No Rachel, no Heather, not even a silly, geeky boy who would like the inside girl I think I am.

OUR LADY OF THE WAITING ROOM

I find Lady of Mercy Hospital by accident. I fall asleep on the bus and miss the mall completely. The hospital is worth a try. Maybe I can learn some pre-med stuff for David.

In a sick kind of way, I love it. There are waiting rooms on almost every floor. I don't want to attract too much attention to myself, so I stay on the move, checking my watch constantly, trying to look as if I have a reason for being here. I'm afraid I'll get caught, but the people around me have other things to worry about. The hospital is the perfect place to be invisible and the cafeteria food is better than the school's.

The worst waiting room is on the heart-attack floor. It is crowded with gray-faced women twisting their wedding rings and watching the doors for a familiar doctor. One lady just sobs, she doesn't care that total strangers watch her nose drip or that people can hear her as soon as they get off the elevator. Her cries stop just short of screaming. They make me shiver. I snag a couple of copies of *People* magazine and I am out of there.

The maternity ward is dangerous because people there are happy. They ask me questions, who am I waiting for, when is the baby due, is it my mother, a sister? If I wanted people to ask me questions, I would have gone to school. I say I have to call my father and flee.

The cafeteria is cool. Huge. Full of people wearing doctor-nurse clothes with college-degree posture and beepers. I always thought hospital people would be real health nuts, but these guys eat junk food like it's going out of style. Big piles of nachos, cheeseburgers as wide as plates, cherry pie, potato chips, all the good stuff. One lone cafeteria worker named Lola stands by the steamed-fish and onion tray. I feel bad for her, so I buy the fish platter. I also buy a plate of mashed potatoes and gravy and a yogurt. I find a seat next to a table of serious, frowning, silver-haired men who use words so long I'm surprised they don't choke. Very official. Nice to hang around people who sound like they know what they're doing.

After lunch I wander up to the fifth floor, to an adult surgery wing where waiting family members concentrate on the television. I sit where I can watch the nurses' station and, beyond that, a couple of hospital rooms. It looks like a good place to get sick. The doctors and nurses seem smart, but they smile every once in a while.

A laundry-room worker pushes an enormous basket of green hospital gowns (the kind that shows your butt if you don't hold it closed) to a storage area. I follow him. If anyone asks, I'm looking for a water fountain. No one asks. I pick up a gown. I want to put it on and crawl under the white knobbly blanket and white sheets in one of those high-off-the-ground beds and sleep. It is getting harder to sleep at home. How long would it take for the nurses to figure out I don't belong here? Would they let me rest for a few days?

A stretcher pushed by a tall guy with muscles sweeps down the hall. One woman walks beside it, a nurse. I have no idea what is wrong with the patient, but his eyes are closed and a thin line of blood seeps through a bandage on his neck.

I put the gown back. There is nothing wrong with me. These are really sick people, sick that you can see. I head for the elevator. The bus is on its way.

CLASH OF THE TITANS

We have a meeting with Principal Principal. Someone has noticed that I've been absent. And that I don't talk. They figure I'm more a head case than a criminal, so they call in the guidance counselor, too.

Mother's mouth twitches with words she doesn't want to say in front of strangers. Dad keeps checking his beeper, hoping someone will call.

I sip water from a paper cup. If the cup were lead crystal, I would open my mouth and take a bite. Crunch, crunch, swallow.

They want me to speak.

"Why won't you say anything?" "For the love of God, open your mouth!" "This is childish, Melinda." "Say something." "You are only hurting yourself by refusing to cooperate." "I don't know why she's doing this to us."

The Principal ha-hums loudly and gets in the middle.

Principal Principal: "We all agree we are here to help. Let's start with these grades. They are not what we expected from you, Melissa."

Dad: "Melinda."

Principal Principal: "Melinda. Last year you were a straight-B student, no behavioral problem, few absences. But the reports I've been getting . . . well, what can we say?"

Mother: "That's the point, she won't *say* anything! I can't get a word out of her. She's mute."

Guidance Counselor: "I think we need to explore the family dynamics at play here."

Mother: "She's jerking us around to get attention."

Me: [inside my head] Would you listen? Would you believe me? Fat chance.

Dad: "Well, something is wrong. What have you done to her? I had a sweet, loving little girl last year, but as soon as she comes up here, she clams up, skips school, and flushes her grades down the toilet. I golf with the school board president, you know."

Mother: "We don't care who you know, Jack. We have to get Melinda to talk."

Guidance Counselor: [leaning forward, looking at Mom and Dad] "Do the two of you have marriage issues?"

Mother responds with unladylike language. Father suggests that the guidance counselor visit that hot, scary underground world. The guidance counselor grows quiet. Maybe she understands why I keep it zipped. Principal Principal sits back in his chair and doodles a hornet.

Tickticktick. I'm missing study hall for this. Nap time. How many days until graduation? I lost track. Have to find a calendar.

Mother and Father apologize. They sing a show tune: "What are we to do? What are we to do? She's so blue, we're just two. What, oh what, are we supposed to do?"

In my headworld, they jump on Principal Principal's desk and perform a tap-dance routine. A spotlight flashes on them. A chorus line joins in, and the guidance counselor dances around a spangled cane. I giggle.

Zap. Back in their world.

Mother: "You think this is funny? We are talking about your future, your life, Melinda!"

Father: "I don't know where you picked up that slacker attitude, but you certainly didn't learn it at home. Probably from the bad influences up here."

G.C.: "Actually, Melinda has some very nice friends. I've seen her helping that group of girls who volunteer so much. Meg Harcutt, Emily Briggs, Siobhan Falon . . ."

Principal Principal: [Stops doodling] "Very nice girls. They all come from good families." He looks at me for the first time and tilts his head to one side. "Those are your friends?"

Do they choose to be so dense? Were they born that way? I have no friends. I have nothing. I say nothing. I am nothing. I wonder how long it takes to ride a bus to Arizona.

MISS

Merryweather In-School Suspension. This is my Consequence. It is in my contract. It's true what they tell you about not signing anything without reading it carefully. Even better, pay a lawyer to read it carefully.

The guidance counselor dreamed up the contract after our cozy get-together in the principal's office. It lists a million things I'm not supposed to do and the consequences I'll suffer if I do them. The consequences for minor offenses like being late to class or not participating were stupid—they wanted me to write an essay—so I took another day off school and Bingo! I earned a trip to MISS.

It's a classroom painted white, with uncomfortable chairs and a lamp that buzzes like an angry hive. The inmates of MISS are commanded to sit and stare at the empty walls. It is supposed to bore us into submission or prepare us for an insane asylum.

Our guard dog today is Mr. Neck. He curls his lip and growls at me. I think this is part of his punishment for that bigoted crap he pulled in class. There are two other convicts with me. One has a cross tattooed on his shaved skull. He sits like a graniteboy waiting for a chisel so he can carve himself out of the mountainside. The other kid looks completely normal. His clothes are a little freaky maybe, but that's a misdemeanor here, not a felony. When Mr. Neck gets up to greet a late arival, the normal-looking kid tells me he likes to start fires.

Our last companion is Andy Evans. My breakfast turns to hydrochloric acid. He grins at Mr. Neck and sits down next to me.

Mr. Neck: "Cutting again, Andy?"

Andy Beast: "No sir. One of your colleagues thinks I have an authority problem. Can you believe it?"

Mr. Neck: "No more talking."

I am BunnyRabbit again, hiding in the open. I sit like I have an egg in my mouth. One move, one word, and the egg will shatter and blow up the world.

I am getting seriously weird in the head.

When Mr. Neck isn't looking, Andy blows in my ear.

I want to kill him.

PICASSO

I can't do anything, not even in art class. Mr. Freeman, a pro at staring out the window himself, thinks he knows what's wrong. "Your imagination is paralyzed," he declares. "You need to take a trip." Ears perk up all over the classroom and someone turns down the radio. A trip? Is he planning a field trip? "You need to visit the mind of a Great One," continues Mr. Freeman. Papers flutter as the class sighs. The radio sings louder again.

He pushes my pitiful linoleum block aside and gently sets down an enormous book. "Picasso." He whispers like a priest. "Picasso. Who saw the truth. Who painted the truth, molded it, ripped from the earth with two angry hands." He pauses. "But I'm getting carried away." I nod. "See Picasso," he commands. "I can't do everything for you. You must walk alone to find your soul."

Blah, blah, yeah. Looking at pictures would be better than watching snow drift. I open the book.

Picasso sure had a thing for naked women. Why not draw them with their clothes on? Who sits around without a shirt on, plucking a mandolin? Why not draw naked guys, just to be fair? Naked women is art, naked guys a no-no, I bet. Probably because most painters are men.

I don't like the first chapters. Besides all the naked women, he painted these blue pictures, like he ran out of red and green for a few weeks. He painted circus people and some dancers who look like they are standing in smog. He should have made them cough.

The next chapter steals my breath away. It takes me out of the room. It confuses me, while one little part of my brain jumps up and down screaming, "I get it! I get it!" Cubism. Seeing beyond what is on the surface. Moving both eyes and a nose to the side of the face. Dicing bodies and tables and guitars as if they were celery sticks, and rearranging them so that you have to really see them to see them. Amazing. What did the world look like to him?

I wish he had gone to high school at Merryweather. I bet we could have hung out. I search the whole book and never see one picture of a tree. Maybe Picasso couldn't do trees either. Why did I get stuck with such a lame idea? I sketch a Cubist tree with hundreds of skinny rectangles for branches. They look like lockers, boxes, glass shards, lips with triangle brown leaves. I drop the sketch on Mr. Freeman's desk. "Now you're getting somewhere," he says. He gives me a thumbs-up.

RIDING SHOTGUN

I am a good girl. I go to every single class for a week. It feels good to know what the teachers are talking about again. My parents get the news flash from the guidance counselor. They aren't sure how to react—happy because I'm behaving, or angrier still that they have to be happy about such a minor thing as a kid who goes to class every day.

The guidance counselor convinces them I need a reward—a chew toy or something. They settle on new clothes. I'm outgrowing everything I own.

But shopping with my mother? Just shoot me and put me out of my misery. Anything but a shopping trip with Mom. She hates shopping with me. At the mall she stalks ahead, chin high, eyelids twitching because I won't try on the practical, "stylish" clothes she likes. Mother is the rock, I am the ocean. I have to pout and roll my eyes for hours until she finally wears down and crumbles into a thousand grains of beach sand. It takes a lot of energy. I don't think I have it in me.

Apparently, Mom isn't up to the drag 'n' whine mall gig either. When they announce I've earned new clothes, they add that I have to get them at Effert's, so Mom can use her discount. I'm supposed to take the bus after school and meet her at the store. In a way, I'm glad. Get in, buy, get out, like ripping off a Band-Aid.

It seems like a good idea until I'm standing at the bus stop in front of school as a blizzard rips through the county. The wind chill must be twenty below and I don't have a hat or mittens. I try keeping my back to the wind, but my rear end freezes. Facing it is impossible. The snow blows up under my eyelids and fills my ears. That's why I don't hear the car pull up next to me. When the horn blows, I nearly jump out of my skin. It's Mr. Freeman. "Need a ride?"

Mr. Freeman's car shocks me. It is a blue Volvo, a safe Swedish box. I had him figured for an old VW bus. It is clean. I had visions of art supplies, posters and rotting fruit everywhere. When I get in, classical music plays quietly. Will wonders never cease.

He says dropping me off in the city is only a little out of his way. He'd love to meet my mother. My eyes widen in fear. "Maybe not," he says. I brush the melting snow from my head and hold my hands in front of the heating vent. He turns the fan up full-blast.

As I thaw, I count the mileage markers on the side of the road, keeping an eye out for interesting roadkill. We get a lot of dead deer in the suburbs. Sometimes poor people take the venison for their winter's meat, but most of the time the carcasses rot until their skin hangs like ribbons over their bones. We head west to the big city.

"You did a good job with that Cubist sketch," he says. I don't know what to say. We pass a dead dog. It doesn't have a collar. "I'm seeing a lot of growth in your work. You are learning more than you know."

Me: "I don't know anything. My trees suck."

Mr. Freeman puts on his turn signal, looks in the rearview mirror, pulls into the left lane, and passes a beer truck. "Don't be so hard on yourself. Art is about making mistakes and learning from them." He pulls back into the right lane.

I watch the beer truck fade into the snowstorm in the side mirror. Part of me thinks maybe he is driving a bit too fast, what with all the snow, but the car is heavy and doesn't slip. The snow that had caked on my socks melts into my sneakers.

Me: "All right, but you said we had to put emotion into our art. I don't know what that means. I don't know what I'm supposed to feel." My fingers fly up and cover my mouth. What am I doing?

Mr. Freeman: "Art without emotion is like chocolate cake without sugar. It makes you gag." He sticks his finger down his throat. "The next time you work on your trees, don't think about trees. Think about love, or hate, or joy, or rage—whatever makes you feel something, makes your palms sweat or your toes curl. Focus on that feeling. When people don't express themselves, they die one piece at a time. You'd be shocked at how many adults are really dead inside—walking through their days with no idea who they are, just waiting for a heart attack or cancer or a Mack truck to come along and finish the job. It's the saddest thing I know."

He pulls off the exit and stops at the light at the bottom of the ramp. Something small and furry and dead is crumpled by the storm sewer. I chew off a scab on my thumb. The Effert's sign blinks in the middle of the block. "Over there," I say. "You can drop me off in front." We sit for a moment, the snow hiding the other side of the street, a cello solo thrumming from the speakers. "Um, thanks," I say. "Don't mention it," he answers. "If you ever need to talk, you know where to find me." I unbuckle the seat belt and open the door.

"Melinda," Mr. Freeman says. Snow filters into the car and melts on the dashboard. "You're a good kid. I think you have a lot to say. I'd like to hear it."

I close the door.

HALL OF MIRRORS

I stop by the manager's office, and the secretary says my mother is on the phone. Just as well. It will be easier to find a pair of jeans without her around. I head for the "Young Ladies" section of the store. (Another reason they don't make any money. Who wants to be called a young lady?)

I need a size ten, as much as it kills me to admit that. Everything I own is an eight or a small. I look at my canoe feet and my wet, obnoxious anklebones. Aren't girls supposed to stop growing at this age?

When I was in sixth grade, my mom bought me all these books about puberty and adolescence, so I would appreciate what a "beautiful" and "natural" and "miraculous" transformation I was going through. Crap. That's what it is. She complains all the time about her hair turning gray and her butt sagging and her skin wrinkling, but I'm supposed to be grateful for a face full of zits, hair in embarrassing places, and feet that grow an inch a night. Utter crap.

No matter what I try on, I know I'll hate it. Effert's has cornered the market on completely unfashionable clothes. Clothes that grandmas buy for your birthday. It's a fashion graveyard. Just get a pair that fits, I tell myself. One pair—that's the goal. I look around. No Mom. I carry three pairs of the least offensive jeans into the dressing room. I am the only person trying anything on. The first pair is way too small—I can't even get them over my butt. I don't bother with the second pair; they are a smaller size. The third pair is huge. Exactly what I'm looking for.

I scurry out to the three-way mirror. With an extra-large sweatshirt over the top, you can hardly tell that they are Effert's jeans. Still no Mom. I adjust the mirror so I can see reflections of reflections, miles and miles of me and my new jeans. I hook my hair behind my ears. I should have washed it. My face is dirty. I lean into the mirror. Eyes after eyes after eyes stare back at me. Am I in there somewhere? A thousand eyes blink. No makeup. Dark circles. I pull the side flaps of the mirror in closer, folding myself into the looking glass and blocking out the rest of the store.

My face becomes a Picasso sketch, my body slicing into dissecting cubes. I saw a movie once where a woman was burned over eighty percent of her body and they had to wash all the dead skin off. They wrapped her in bandages, kept her drugged, and waited for skin grafts. They actually sewed her into a new skin.

I push my ragged mouth against the mirror. A thousand bleeding, crusted lips push back. What does it feel like to walk in a new skin? Was she completely sensitive like a baby, or numb, without nerve endings, just walking in a skin bag? I exhale and my mouth disappears in a fog. I feel like my skin has been burned off. I stumble from thornbush to thornbush—my mother and father who hate each other, Rachel who hates me, a school that gags on me like I'm a hairball. And Heather.

I just need to hang on long enough for my new skin to graft. Mr. Freeman thinks I need to find my feelings. How can I not find them? They are chewing me alive like an infestation of thoughts, shame, mistakes. I squeeze my eyes shut. Jeans that fit, that's a good start. I have to stay away from the closet, go to all my classes. I will make myself normal. Forget the rest of it.

GERMINATION

We've finished the plant unit in biology. Ms. Keen drops ten-pound hints that the test will focus on seeds. I study.

How seeds get planted: This is actually cool. Some plants spit their seeds into the wind. Others make seeds yummy enough for birds to eat, so they get pooped out on passing cars. Plants make way more seeds than they need, because they know that life is not perfect and all the seeds won't make it. Kind of smart, when you think about it. People used to do that, too— have twelve or fifteen kids because they figured some would die, some would turn out rotten, and a couple would be hard-working, honest farmers. Who knew how to plant seeds.

What seeds need to germinate: Seeds are inefficient. If the seed is planted too deep, it doesn't warm up at the right time. Plant it too close to the surface and a crow eats it. Too much rain and the seed molds. Not enough rain and it never gets started. Even if it does manage to sprout, it can be choked by weeds, rooted up by a dog, mashed by a soccer ball, or asphyxiated by car exhaust.

It's amazing anything survives.

How plants grow: Quickly. Most plants grow fast and die young. People get seventy years, a bean plant gets four months, maybe five. Once the itty-bitty baby plant peeks out of the ground, it sprouts leaves, so it can absorb more sun. Then it sleeps, eats, and sunbathes until it's ready to flower— a teenage plant. This is a bad time to be a rose or a zinnia or a marigold, because people attack with scissors and cut off what's pretty. But plants are cool. If the rose is picked, the plant grows another one. It needs to bloom to produce more seeds.

I am going to ace this test.

BOLOGNA EXILE

My cafeteria strategy has changed since I have no friends in the known universe. First off, I don't go through the line for anything, to avoid that vulnerable moment of coming out into the lunchroom, that moment when every head lifts and evaluates: friend, enemy, or loser.

So I brown-bag it. I had to write a note to my mother asking her to buy lunch bags, bologna, and little containers of applesauce. The note made her happy. She came home from the store with all kinds of junk food I could take. Maybe I should start talking to Them, maybe a little bit. But what if I say the wrong thing?

Bologna girl, that's me.

I try to read while eating alone, but the noise gets between my eyes and the page and I can't see through it. I observe. I pretend I'm a scientist, on the outside looking in, the way Ms. Keen describes her days watching rats get lost in mazes.

The Marthas don't look lost. They sit in formation, a new girl in my old seat—a sophomore who just moved here from Oregon. Her clothes have a dangerously high percentage of polyester. She needs to get that taken care of. They nibble carrot sticks and olives, spread pâté onto stone-ground wheat crackers and trade bites of goat cheese. Meg 'n' Emily 'n' Heather drink cranberry-apricot juice. Too bad I can't buy stock in the juice company—I am watching a trend in the making.

Are they talking about me? They're certainly laughing enough. I chomp my sandwich and it barfs mustard on my shirt. Maybe they're planning the next Project. They could mail snowballs to the weather-deprived children in Texas. They could knit goat-hair blankets for shorn sheep. I imagine what Heather might look like in ten years, after two children and seventy pounds. It helps a little.

Rachel/Rachelle takes a seat at the end of my table with Hana, the exchange student from Egypt. Rachel/Rachelle is now experimenting with Islam. She wears a scarf on her head and some brown-and-red gauzy harem pants. Her eyes are ringed with black eyeliner thick as crayon. I think I see her looking at me, but I'm probably wrong. Hana wears jeans and a Gap T-shirt. They eat hummus and pita and titter in French.

There is a sprinkling of losers like me scattered among the happy teenagers, prunes in the oatmeal of school. The others have the social power to sit with other losers. I'm the only one sitting alone, under the glowing neon sign which reads, "Complete and Total Loser, Not Quite Sane. Stay Away. Do Not Feed."

I go to the rest room to turn my shirt around so the mustard stain is hidden under my hair.

SNOW DAY—SCHOOL AS USUAL

We had eight inches of snow last night. In any other part of the country, that would mean a snow day. Not in Syracuse. We never get snow days. It snows an inch in South Carolina, everything shuts down and they get on the six o'clock news. In our district, they plow early and often and put chains on the bus tires.

Hairwoman tells us they canceled school for a whole week back in the seventies because of the energy crisis. It was wicked cold and would have cost too much to heat the school. She looks wistful. Wistful—one-point vocab word. She blows her nose loudly and pops another smelly green cough drop. The wind blasts a snowdrift against the window.

Our teachers need a snow day. They look unusually pale. The men aren't shaving carefully and the women never remove their boots. They suffer some sort of teacherflu. Their noses drip, their throats gum up, their eyes are rimmed with red. They come to school long enough to infect the staff room, then go home sick when the sub shows up.

Hairwoman: "Open your books, now. Who can tell me what snow symbolized to Hawthorne?"

Class: "Groan."

Hawthorne wanted snow to symbolize cold, that's what I think. Cold and silence. Nothing quieter than snow. The sky screams to deliver it, a hundred banshees flying on the edge of the blizzard. But once the snow covers the ground, it hushes as still as my heart.

STUPID STUPID

I sneak into my closet after school because I can't face the idea of riding home on a busful of sweaty, smiling teeth sucking up my oxygen. I say hello to my poster of Maya and my Cubist tree. My turkey-bone scupture has fallen down again. I prop it up on the shelf next to the mirror. It slides back down and lies flat. I leave it there and curl up in my chair. The closet is warm and I'm ready for a nap. I've been having trouble sleeping at home. I wake up because the covers are on the floor or because I'm standing at the kitchen door, trying to get out. It feels safer in my little hideaway. I doze off.

I wake to the sound of girls screaming, "Be Aggressive, BE-BE Aggressive! B-E A-G-G-R-E-S-S-I-V-E!"

For a minute there, I think that I've tripped into the land of the truly insane, but then a crowd roars. It is a basketball game, last game of the season. I check my watch—8:45. I've been asleep for hours. I grab my backpack and fly down the hall.

The noise of the gym pulls me in. I stand by the door for the last minute of the game. The crowd chants down the last seconds like it's New Year's Eve, then explode from the stands like angry hornets at the sound of the buzzer. We won, beating the Coatesville Cougars 51–50. The cheerleaders weep. The coaches embrace. I get caught up in the excitement and clap like a little girl.

This is my mistake, thinking I belong. I should have bolted for home immediately. But I don't. I hang around. I want to be a part of it all.

David Petrakis pushes toward the doors in the middle of a group of friends. He sees me looking at him and detaches himself from his pod.

David: "Melinda! Where were you sitting? Did you see that last shot? Unbelievable!! Unbefreakinglievable." He dribbles an imaginary ball on the ground, fakes left, right, then pulls up for a shot. David should stick to human-rights abuses. He goes on and on, a loose ball racing downhill. To hear him talk, you'd think they just won the NBA championship. Then he invites me back to his house for celebratory pizza.

David: "Come on, Mel. You gotta come with us! My dad told me to bring anyone I wanted. We can give you a ride home after if you want. It'll be fun. You do remember fun, don't you?"

Nope. I don't do parties. No thanks. I trot out excuses: homework, strict parents, tuba practice, late-night dentist appointment, have to feed the warthogs. I don't have a good track record with parties.

David doesn't bother to analyze my reluctance. If he were a girl, maybe he would have pleaded or whined more. Guys don't do that. Yes/no. Stay/go. Suit yourself. See you Monday.

I think it's some kind of psychiatric disorder when you have more than one personality in your head. That's what it feels like when I walk home. The two Melindas fight every step of the way. Melinda One is pissed that she couldn't go to the party.

Melinda One: "Get a life. It was just pizza. He wasn't going to try anything. His parents were going to be there! You worry too much. You're never going to let us have any fun, are you? You're going to turn into one of those weird old ladies who has a hundred cats and calls the cops when kids cut across her back yard. I can't stand you."

Melinda Two waits for One to finish her tantrum. Two carefully watches the bushes along the sidewalk for a lurking bogeyman or worse.

Melinda Two: "The world is a dangerous place. You don't know what would have happened. What if he was just saying his parents were going to be there? He could have been lying. You can never tell when people are lying. Assume the worst. Plan for disaster. Now hurry up and get us home. I don't like it out here. It's too dark."

If I kick both of them out of my head, who would be left?

A NIGHT TO REMEMBER

I can't sleep after the game. Again. I spend a couple hours tuning AM radio to the weird bounces of night. I listen to jabber-jabber from Quebec, a farm report from Minnesota, and a country station in Nashville. I crawl out my window onto the porch roof and wrap myself in all my blankets.

A fat white seed sleeps in the sky.

Slush is frozen over. People say that winter lasts forever, but it's because they obsess over the thermometer. North in the mountains, the maple syrup is trickling. Brave geese punch through the thin ice left on the lake. Underground, pale seeds roll over in their sleep. Starting to get restless. Starting to dream green.

The moon looked closer back in August.

Rachel got us to the end-of-summer party, a cheerleader party, with beer and seniors and music. She blackmailed her brother, Jimmy, to drive us. We were all sleeping over at Rachel's house. Her mother thought Jimmy was taking us roller-skating.

It was at a farm a couple of miles from our development. The kegs were in the barn where the speakers were set up. Most people hung at the edge of the lights. They looked like models in a blue-jeans ad, thinthinthin, big lips, big earrings, white smiles. I felt like such a little kid.

Rachel found a way to fit in, of course. She knew a lot of people because of Jimmy. I tasted a beer. It was worse than cough medicine. I gulped it down. Another beer and one more, then I worried I would throw up. I walked out of the crowd, toward the woods. The moon shone on the leaves. I could see the lights, like stars strung in the pines. Somebody giggled, hidden beyond the dark, quiet boygirl whispers. I couldn't see them.

A step behind me. A senior. And then he was talking to me, flirting with me. This gorgeous cover-model guy. His hair was way better than mine, his every inch a tanned muscle, and he had straight white teeth. Flirting with me! Where was Rachel—she had to see this!

Greek God: "Where did you come from? You're too beautiful to hide in the dark. Come dance with me."

He took my hand and pulled me close to him. I breathed in cologne and beer and something I couldn't identify. I fit in against his body perfectly, my head level with his shoulder. I was a little dizzy—I laid my cheek on his chest. He wrapped one arm around my back. His other hand slid down to my butt. I thought that was a little rude, but my tongue was thick with beer and I couldn't figure out how to tell him to slow down. The music was sweet. This was what high school was supposed to feel like. Where was Rachel? She had to see this!

He tilted my face up to his. He kissed me, man kiss, hard sweet and deep. Nearly knocked me off my feet, that kiss. And I thought for just a minute there that I had a boyfriend, I would start high school with a boyfriend, older and stronger and ready to watch out for me. He kissed me again. His teeth ground hard against my lips. It was hard to breathe.

A cloud cloaked the moon. Shadows looked like photo negatives.

"Do you want to?" he asked.

What did he say? I didn't answer. I didn't know. I didn't speak.

We were on the ground. When did that happen? "No." No I did not like this. I was on the ground and he was on top of me. My lips mumble something about leaving, about a friend who needs me, about my parents worrying. I can hear myself—I'm mumbling like a deranged drunk. His lips lock on mine and I can't say anything. I twist my head away. He is so heavy. There is a boulder on me. I open my mouth to breathe, to scream, and his hand covers it. In my head, my voice is as clear as a bell: "NO I DON'T WANT TO!" But I can't spit it out. I'm trying to remember how we got on the ground and where the moon went and wham! shirt up, shorts down, and the ground smells wet and dark and NO!—I'm not really here, I'm definitely back at Rachel's, crimping my hair and gluing on fake nails, and he smells like beer and mean and he hurts me hurts me hurts me and gets up and zips his jeans

and smiles.

The next thing I saw was the telephone. I stood in the middle of a drunken crowd and I called 911 because I needed help. All those visits from Officer Friendly in second grade paid off. A lady answered the phone, "Police, state your emergency," and I saw my face in the window over the kitchen sink and no words came out of my mouth. Who was that girl? I had never seen her before. Tears oozed down my face, over my bruised lips, pooling on the handset. "It's OK," said the nice lady on the phone. "We have your location. Officers are on the way. Are you hurt? Are you being threatened?" Someone grabbed the phone from my hands and listened. A scream—the cops were coming! Blue and cherry lights flashing in the kitchen-sink window. Rachel's face—so angry—in mine. Someone slapped me. I crawled out of the room through a forest of legs. Outside, the moon smiled goodbye and slipped away.

I walked home to an empty house. Without a word.

It isn't August. The moon is asleep and I'm sitting on my porch roof like a frozen gargoyle, wondering if the sun is going to blow off the world today and sleep in.

There is blood on the snow. I bit my lip clear through. It needs stitches. Mom will be late again. I hate winter. I've lived in Syracuse my whole life and I hate winter. It starts too early and ends too late. No one likes it. Why does anyone stay here?

MY REPORT CARD:

Social Life	F	Social Studies	F	Spanish	D	Art	A
Lunch	D	Biology	D+	Algebra	F		
Clothes	F	English	D+	Gym	D		

FOURTH MARKING PERIOD

EXTERMINATORS

The PTA has started a petition to get rid of the Hornet as our school mascot. It was the cheer that got to them. They heard it at the last basketball game.

> "WE ARE THE HORNETS,
> HORNY, HORNY HORNETS!
> EVERYWHERE WE GO-OH,
> PEOPLE WANT TO KNO-OOW,
> WHO WE ARE, SO WE TELL THEM . . .
> WE ARE THE HORNETS,
> HORNY, HORNY HORNETS!
> (and on and on and on)

The wiggles and shakes that accompany the cheer freaked out the Merryweather PTA. Freaked out PTAs all over the city when the Horny Hornet cheer was televised. The TV sports guy thought the song was cute, so he did a segment showing the "Hornet Hustle," with the cheerleaders shaking their stingers, and the crowd bumping and grinding their horny Hornet heinies.

The student council started a counterpetition. The Honor Society wrote it. It describes the psychological harm we have all suffered from this year's lack of identity. It pleads for consistency, stability. It's pretty good: "We, the students of Merryweather High, have become proud of our Hornet selves. We are tenacious, stinging, clever. We are a hive, a community of students. Don't take away our Hornetdom. We *are* Hornets."

It won't be a real issue until football starts up again. Our baseball team always stinks.

THE WET SEASON

Spring is on the way. The winter rats—rusty brown $700 cars that everyone with sense drives from November until April— are rolling back into storage. The snow is melting for good and the pretty-baby shiny cars glitter in the senior parking lot.

There are other signs of spring. Front lawns cough up the shovels and mittens that were gobbled by snowdrifts in January. My mother moved the winter coats up to the attic. Dad's been mumbling about the storm windows, but hasn't taken them down. From the bus I saw a farmer walking his field, waiting for the mud to tell him when to plant.

April Fool's Day is when most seniors get their acceptance or rejection letters from college. Thumbs up or thumbs down. It's a sick piece of timing. Tensions are running high. Kids drink pink stomach medicine from the bottle. David Petrakis My Lab Partner is writing a database program to track who got in where. He wants to analyze which advanced-placement classes the seniors took, their standardized test scores, extracurriculars, and GPAs to figure out what he needs to do to get into Harvard.

I've been going to most of my classes. Good girl, Mellie. Roll over, Mellie. Sit, Mellie. No one has patted me on the head, though. I passed an algebra test, I passed an English test, I passed a biology test. Well, hallelujah. It is all so profoundly stupid. Maybe this is why kids join clubs—to give them something to think about during class.

Andy Beast joined the International Club. I hadn't figured him for a deep interest in Greek cooking or French museums. He has abandoned the Martha table and hangs around and onto Rachel/Rachelle and Greta–Ingrid and all the other resident aliens. Rachel/Rachelle flutters her purple eyelashes at him like he's some kind of Überdude. You'd think she'd have more sense.

Easter came and went without much notice. I think it caught my mother by surprise. She doesn't like Easter because the date keeps shifting and it's not a big shopping holiday. When I was a kid, Mom used to hide colored eggs for me all over the house. The last egg was inside a big basket of chocolate rabbits and yellow marshmallow chicks. Before my grandparents died, they would take me to church and I would wear stiff dresses with itchy lace.

This year we celebrated by eating lamb chops. I made hard-boiled eggs for lunch and drew little faces on them with a black pen. Dad complained about how much yard work has to be done. Mom didn't say much. I said less. In heaven, my grandparents frowned. I sort of wished we had gone to church. Some of the Easter songs are pretty.

SPRING BREAK

It is the last day of Spring Break. My house is shrinking and I feel like Alice in Wonderland. Afraid that my head might burst through the roof, I head for the mall. I have ten bucks in my pocket—what to spend it on? French fries—ten dollars' worth of french fries, ultimate fantasy. If *Alice in Wonderland* were written today, I bet she'd have a supersized order of fries that said "Eat me," instead of a small cake. On the other hand, we're rushing toward summer, which means shorts and T-shirts and maybe even a bathing suit now and then. I walk past the deep-fat fryers.

Now that spring is past, the fall fashions are in the store windows. I keep waiting for the year when the fashions catch up to the seasons. A couple of stores have performance artists hanging at the front door. One guy keeps flying a stupid loop-the-loop airplane; a plastic-faced woman keeps tying and retying a shawl. No, now it's a skirt. Now it's a halter top. Now it's a head scarf. People avoid looking at her, as if they aren't sure if they should applaud or tip her. I feel bad for her—I wonder what her grades were in high school. I want to give her a tip, only it would be rude to ask if she has change for a ten.

I ride the escalator down to the central fountain, where today's entertainment is face-painting. The line is long and loud—six-year-olds and their mothers. A little girl walks past me—she's a tiger. She's crying about ice cream and she wipes her tears. Her tiger paint smears and her mom yells at her.

"What a zoo."

I turn. Ivy is sitting on the edge of the fountain, a giant sketchbook balanced on her knees. She nods toward the line of whiners and the face painters furiously coloring stripes, spots, and whiskers.

"I feel bad for them," I say. "What are you drawing?"

Ivy moves so I can sit next to her and hands me the sketchbook. She's drawing the kids' faces. Half of each face is plain and sad, the other half is plastered with thick clown makeup that is fake-happy. She hasn't painted any tigers or leopards.

"The last time I was here, they were doing clown faces. No such luck today," Ivy explains.

"Looks good, though," I say. "It's kind of spooky. Not creepy, but unexpected." I hand back the sketchbook.

Ivy pokes her pencil into her bun. "Good. That's what I'm trying for. That turkey-bone thing you did was creepy, too. Creepy in a good way, good creepy. It's been months and I'm still thinking about it."

What am I supposed to say now? I bite my lip, then release it. I pull a roll of Life Savers from my pocket. "Want a piece?" She takes one, I take three, and we suck in silence for a moment.

"How's the tree coming?" she asks.

I groan. "Stinks. It was a mistake to sign up for art. I just couldn't see myself taking wood shop."

"You're better than you think you are," Ivy says. She opens to an empty page in the sketchbook. "I don't know why you keep using a linoleum block. If I were you, I'd just let it out, draw. Here—try a tree."

We sit there trading pencils. I draw a trunk, Ivy adds a branch, I extend the branch, but it is too long and spindly. I start to erase it, but Ivy stops me. "It's fine the way it is, it just needs some leaves. Layer the leaves and make them slightly different sizes and it will look great. You have a great start there."

She's right.

GENETICS

The last unit of the year in biology is genetics. It's impossible to listen to Ms. Keen. Her voice sounds like a cold engine that won't turn over. The lecture starts with some priest named Greg who studied vegetables, and ends up with an argument about blue eyes. I think I missed something—how did we leap from veggies to eye color? I'll copy David's notes.

I flip ahead in the textbook. There's an interesting chapter about acid rain. Nothing about sex. We aren't scheduled to learn about that until eleventh grade.

David draws a chart in his notebook. I snap my pencil point and walk to the front of the room to sharpen it. I figure the walk will do me good. Ms. Keen sputters on. We get half our genes from our mother and half from our father. I thought my jeans came from Effert's. Ha-ha, biology joke.

Mom says I take after Dad's side of the family. They're mostly cops and insurance salesmen who bet on football games and smoke disgusting cigars. Dad says I take after Mom's side of the family. They're farmers who grow rocks and poison ivy. They don't say much, visit dentists, or read.

When I was a little kid, I used to pretend I was a princess who had been adopted when my kingdom was overrun by bad guys. Any day my real parents, Mr. King and Mrs. Queen, would send the royal limo to pick me up. I just about had a seven-year-old heart attack when my dad took a limo to the airport the first time. I thought they had really come to take me away and I didn't want to go. Dad took taxis after that.

I look out the window. No limos. No chariots or carriages. Now, when I really want to leave, no one will give me a ride.

I sketch a willow tree drooping into the water. I won't show it to Mr. Freeman. This one is for my closet. I've been taping some of my drawings on the walls. Any more classes as boring as this one and I'll be ready to move back in there full-time. My leaves are good, natural. The trick is to make them different sizes, and then crowd them one on top of another. Ivy was right.

Ms. Keen writes "Dominant/Recessive" on the board. I look at David's notes. He's drawing a family tree. David got his hair gene from his dad and his eye gene from his mom. I draw a family tree. A family stump. There aren't that many of us. I can barely remember their names. Uncle Jim, Uncle Thomas, Aunt Mary, Aunt Kathy—there's another aunt, she is very recessive. She recessed herself all the way to Peru. I think I have her eyes. I got my "I don't want to know about it" gene from my dad and my "I'll think about it tomorrow" gene from my mom.

Ms. Keen says we'll have a quiz the next day. I wish I had paid attention during class. I wish I were adopted. I wish David would quit sighing when I ask to copy his notes.

TEN MORE LIES THEY TELL YOU IN HIGH SCHOOL
1. You will use algebra in your adult lives.
2. Driving to school is a privilege that can be taken away.
3. Students must stay on campus for lunch.
4. The new textbooks will arrive any day now.
5. Colleges care about more than your SAT scores.
6. We are enforcing the dress code.
7. We will figure out how to turn off the heat soon.
8. Our bus drivers are highly trained professionals.
9. There is nothing wrong with summer school.
10. We want to hear what you have to say.

MY LIFE AS A SPY

Rachel/Rachelle has lost her mind. She has flipped. She went to the movies with Andy Beast and her exchange friends and now she follows after him, panting like a bichon frise. He wears her buddy Greta–Ingrid draped around his neck like a white scarf. When he spits, I bet Rachel/Rachelle catches it in a cup and saves it.

Rachel/Rachelle and some other twit natter about the movie date before Mr. Stetman starts class. I want to puke. Rachel/Rachelle is just "Andythis" and "Andythat." Could she be more obvious? I close my ears to her stupid asthmatic laugh and work on the homework that was due yesterday.

It is usually easy to do homework in class because Mr. Stetman's voice creates a gentle, white-noise sound barrier. I can't do it today, I can't escape the arguments circling my head. Why worry about Rachel/Rachelle? (He'll hurt her.) Had she done a single decent thing for me the whole year? (She was my best friend through middle school, that counts for something.) No, she's a witch and a traitor. (She didn't see what happened.) Let her lust after the Beast; I hope he breaks her heart. (What if he breaks something else?)

When class is over, I slide into the middle of the pack pushing out the door before Mr. Stetman can bust me for the homework. Rachel/Rachelle shoves past me to where Greta–Ingrid and a short kid from Belgium are waiting. I tail them, always keeping two bodies between us like the detectives on television. They're on their way to the foreign-language wing. That's no surprise. The foreign kids are always there, like they need to breathe air scented with their native language a couple times a day or they'll choke to death on too much American.

Andy Beast swoops over their heads, folds his wings, and sets himself between the girls as they start up the stairs. He tries to kiss Greta–Ingrid's cheek, but she turns away. He kisses Rachel/Rachelle's cheek and she giggles. He does not kiss the cheek of the short Belgian. The Belgian and the Swede wave "ciao" at the office of the Foreign Language Department. Rumor has it that there is an espresso maker in there.

The friendly momentum keeps Rachel/Rachelle and Andy walking all the way to the end of the hall. I face a corner and pretend to study algebra. I figure that's enough to make me unrecognizable. They sit on the floor, Rachel/Rachelle in a full lotus. Andy steals Rachel/Rachelle's notebook. She whines like a baby and throws herself across his lap to get it back. I shiver with goose bumps. He tosses the notebook from one hand to the other, always keeping it just out of her reach. Then he says something to her. I can't hear it. The hall sounds like a packed football stadium. His lips move poison and she smiles and then she kisses him wet. Not a Girl Scout kiss. He gives her the notebook. His lips move. Lava spills out my ears. She is not any part of a pretend Rachelle-chick. I can only see third-grade Rachel who liked barbecue potato chips and who braided pink embroidery thread into my hair that I wore for months until my mom made me cut it out. I rest my forehead against the prickly stucco.

THIN ATMOSPHERE

The best place to figure this out is my closet, my throne room, my foster home. I want a shower. Maybe I should tell

Greta–Ingrid. (My Swedish isn't good enough.) I could talk to Rachel. (Yeah, right.) I could say I'd heard bad things about Andy. (It would only make him more attractive.) I could maybe tell her what happened. (As if she'd listen. What if she told Andy? What would he do?)

There isn't much room for pacing. I take two steps, turn, two steps back. I bang my shin against the chair. Stupid room. What a dumb idea, sitting in a closet like this. I flop in the chair. It whooshes out old janitor smells—feet, beef jerky, shirts left in the washer too long. The turkey-bone sculpture gives off a faint rotting odor. Three baby-food jars of potpourri don't make a dent in the stink. Maybe there's a dead rat decomposing in the wall, right near the hot-air vent.

Maya Angelou watches me, two fingers on the side of her face. It is an intelligent pose. Maya wants me to tell Rachel.

I take off my sweatshirt. My T-shirt sticks to me. They still have the heat running full-blast even though it's warm enough to crack open the windows. That's what I need, a window. As much as I complain about winter, cold air is easier to breathe, slipping like silver mercury down my lungs and out again. April is humid, with slush evaporating or rain drizzling. A warm, moldy washcloth of a month.

The edges of my pictures curl in the damp. There has been some progress in this whole tree project, I guess. Like Picasso, I've gone through different phases. There's the Confused Period, when I wasn't sure what the assignment really was. The Spaz Period, when I couldn't draw a tree to save my life. The Dead Period, when all my trees looked like they had been through a forest fire or a blight. I'm getting better. Don't know what to call this phase yet. All these drawings make the closet seem smaller. Maybe I should bribe a janitor to haul all this stuff to my house, make my bedroom more like this, more like home.

Maya taps me on the shoulder. I'm not listening. I know I know, I don't want to hear it. I need to do something about Rachel, something for her. Maya tells me without saying anything. I stall. Rachel will hate me. (She already hates me.) She won't listen. (I have to try.) I groan and rip out a piece of notebook paper. I write her a note, a left-handed note, so she won't know it's from me.

"Andy Evans will use you. He is not what he pretends to be. I heard he attacked a ninth-grader. Be very, very careful. A Friend. P.S. Tell Greta–Ingrid, too."

I didn't want the Swedish supermodel on my conscience either.

GROWING PAINS

Mr. Freeman is a jerk. Instead of leaving me alone to "find my muse" (a real quote, I swear), he lands on the stool next to me and starts criticizing. What is wrong with my tree? He overflows with words describing how bad it sucks. It's stiff, unnatural, it doesn't flow. It is an insult to trees everywhere.

I agree. My tree is hopeless. It isn't art; it's an excuse not to take sewing class. I don't belong in Mr. Freeman's room any more than I belong in the Marthas or in my little-girl pink bedroom. This is where the real artists belong, like Ivy. I carry the linoleum block to the garbage can and throw it in hard enough to make everyone look at me. Ivy frowns through her wire sculpture. I sit back down and lay my head on the table. Mr. Freeman retrieves the block from the garbage. He brings back the Kleenex box, too. How could he tell I was crying?

Mr. Freeman: "You are getting better at this, but it's not good enough. This looks like a tree, but it is an average, ordinary, everyday, boring tree. Breathe life into it. Make it bend—trees are flexible, so they don't snap. Scar it, give it a twisted branch—perfect trees don't exist. Nothing is perfect. Flaws are interesting. Be the tree."

He has this ice-cream voice like a kindergarten teacher. If he thinks I can do it, then I'll try one more time. My fingers tip-tip over to the linoleum knife. Mr. Freeman pats my shoulder once, then turns to make someone else miserable. I wait until he isn't watching, then try to carve life into my flat linoleum square.

Maybe I could carve off all the linoleum and call it "Empty Block." If a famous person did that, it would probably be really popular and sell for a fortune. If I do it, I'll flunk. "Be the tree." What kind of advice is that? Mr. Freeman has been hanging out with too many New Age weirdos. I was a tree in the second-grade play because I made a bad sheep. I stood there with my arms outstretched like branches and my head drooping in the breeze. It gave me sore arms. I doubt trees are ever told to "be the screwed-up ninth-grader."

GAG ORDER

David Petrakis's lawyer had a meeting with Mr. Neck and some kind of teacher lawyer. Guess who won. I bet David could skip class the rest of the year if he wanted and still get an A. Which he would never do. But you better believe that whenever David raises his hand, Mr. Neck lets him talk as much as he wants. David, quiet David, is full of long, drawn-out, rambling opinions about social studies. The rest of the class is grateful. We bow down to the Almighty David, Who Keeps the Neck Off Our Backs.

Unfortunately, Mr. Neck still gives tests, and most of us fail them. Mr. Neck makes an announcement: anyone who is flunking can write an extra-credit report on a Cultural Influence at the Turn of the Century. (He skipped the Industrial Revolution so he could drag our class past the year 1900.) He does not want all of us in summer school.

I don't want to see him in summer school either. I write about the suffragettes. Before the suffragettes came along, women were treated like dogs.

> *Women could not vote
> *Women could not own property
> *Women were not allowed in many schools

They were dolls, with no thoughts, or opinions, or voices of their own. Then the suffragettes marched in, full of loud, in-your-face ideas. They got arrested and thrown in jail, but nothing shut them up. They fought and fought until they earned the rights they should have had all along.

I write the best report ever. Anything I copy from a book, I put in quotes and footnotes (feetnote?). I use books, magazine articles, and a videotape. I think about looking for an old suffragette in a nursing home, but they are probably all dead.

I even hand it in on time. Mr. Neck scowls. He looks down on me and says, "To get credit for the report, you have to deliver it orally. Tomorrow. At the beginning of class."

Me:

NO JUSTICE, NO PEACE

There is no way I'm reading my suffragette report in front of the class. That wasn't part of the original assignment. Mr. Neck changed it at the very last second because he wants to flunk me or hates me or something. But I've written a really good report and I'm not going to let an idiot teacher jerk me around like this. I ask David Petrakis for advice. We come up with a Plan.

I get to class early, when Mr. Neck is still in the lounge. I write what I need to on the board and cover the words with a suffragette protest sign. My box from the copy shop is on the floor. Mr. Neck walks in. He grumbles that I can go first. I stand suffragette tall and calm. It is a lie. My insides feel like

I'm caught in a tornado. My toes curl inside my sneakers, trying to grip the floor so I won't get sucked out the window.

Mr. Neck nods at me. I pick up my report as if I'm going to read it out loud. I stand there, papers trembling as if a breeze is blowing through the closed door. I turn around and rip my poster off the blackboard.

THE SUFFRAGETTES FOUGHT FOR THE RIGHT TO SPEAK.
THEY WERE ATTACKED, ARRESTED, AND THROWN IN JAIL
FOR DARING TO DO WHAT THEY WANTED. LIKE THEY WERE,
I AM WILLING TO STAND UP FOR WHAT I BELIEVE. NO ONE
SHOULD BE FORCED TO GIVE SPEECHES. I CHOOSE TO STAY
SILENT.

The class reads slowly, some of them moving their lips. Mr. Neck turns around to see what everyone is staring at. I nod at David. He joins me at the front of the room and I hand him my box.

David: "Melinda has to deliver her report to the class as part of the assignment. She made copies everyone can read."

He passes out the copies. They cost me $6.72 at the office-supply store. I was going to make a cover page and color it, but I haven't gotten much allowance recently, so I just put the title at the top of the first page.

My plan is to stand in front of the class for the five minutes I was given for my presentation. The suffragettes must have planned out and timed their protests, too. Mr. Neck has other plans. He gives me a D and escorts me to the authorities. I forgot about how the suffragettes were hauled off to jail. Duh. I go on a tour of the guidance counselor's office, Principal Principal's, and wind up back in MISS. I am back to being a Discipline Problem again.

I need a lawyer. I showed up every day this semester, sat my butt in every class, did some homework, and didn't cheat on tests. I still get slammed in MISS. There is no way they can punish me for not speaking. It isn't fair. What do they know about me? What do they know about the inside of my head? Flashes of lightning, children crying. Caught in an avalanche, pinned by worry, squirming under the weight of doubt, guilt. Fear.

The walls in MISS are still white. Andy Beast isn't here. Thank God for small favors. A boy with lime-colored hair who looks like he's channeling for an alien species dozes; two Goths in black velvet dresses and artfully torn pantyhose trade Mona Lisa smiles. They cut school to stand in line for killer concert tickets. MISS is a small price to pay for Row 10, seats 21 and 22.

I simmer. Lawyers on TV always tell their clients not to say anything. The cops say that thing: "Anything you say will be used against you." Self-incrimination. I looked it up. Three-point vocab word. So why does everyone make such a big hairy deal about me not talking? Maybe I don't want to incriminate myself. Maybe I don't like the sound of my voice. Maybe I don't have anything to say.

The boy with the lime-colored hair wakes up when he falls out of his chair. The Gothgirls whinny. Mr. Neck picks his nose when he thinks we aren't looking. I need a lawyer.

ADVICE FROM A SMART MOUTH

David Petrakis sends me a note in social studies. Typed. He thinks it's horrible that my parents didn't videotape Mr. Neck's class or stick up for me the way his folks did. It feels so good to have someone feel sorry for me, I don't mention that my parents don't know what happened. They'll figure out what happened soon enough at the next meeting with the guidance counselor.

I think David should be a judge. His latest career goal is to be a quantum-physics genius. I don't know what that means, but he says his father is furious. His dad is right—David was made for the law: deadly calm, turbo-charged brain, and a good eye for weakness.

He stops by my locker. I tell him Mr. Neck gave me a D for the suffragette report.

David: "He has a point."

Me: "It was a great report! You read it. I wrote a bibliography and I didn't copy from the encyclopedia. It was the best report ever. It's not my fault Mr. Neck doesn't get performance art."

David pauses to offer me a stick of gum. It's a delaying tactic, the kind that juries love.

David: "But you got it wrong. The suffragettes were all about speaking up, screaming for their rights. You can't speak up for your right to be silent. That's letting the bad guys win. If the suffragettes did that, women wouldn't be able to vote yet."

I blow a bubble in his face. He folds the gum wrappers into tiny triangles.

David: "Don't get me wrong. I think what you did was kind of cool and getting stuck in MISS wasn't fair. But don't expect to make a difference unless you speak up for yourself."

Me: "Do you lecture all your friends like this?"

David: "Only the ones I like."

We both chew on this for a minute. The bell rings. I keep looking in my locker for a book that I already know isn't there. David checks his watch a hundred times. We hear Principal Principal bellow, "Let's move it, people!"

David: "Maybe I'll call you."

Me: "Maybe I won't answer." Chew, chew. Blowbubblepop. "Maybe I will."

Is he asking me out? I don't think so. But he kind of is. I guess I'll answer if he calls. But if he touches me I'll explode, so a date is out of the question. No touching.

THE BEAST PROWLS

I stay after school to work on tree sketches. Mr. Freeman helps me for a while. He gives me a roll of brown paper and a piece of white chalk and shows me how to draw a tree in three sweeping lines. He doesn't care how many mistakes I make, just one-two-three, "like a waltz," he says. Over and over. I use up a mile of the paper, but he doesn't care. This may be the root of his budget problem with the school board.

God crackles over the intercom and tells Mr. Freeman he's late for a faculty meeting. Mr. Freeman says the kind of words you don't usually hear from teachers. He gives me a new piece of chalk and tells me to draw roots. You can't grow a decent tree without roots.

The art room is one of the places I feel safe. I hum and don't worry about looking stupid. Roots. Ugh. But I try. One-two-three, one-two-three. I don't worry about the next day or minute. One-two-three.

Somebody flicks the lights off. My head snaps up. IT is there. Andy Beast. Little rabbit heart leaps out of my chest and scampers across the paper, leaving bloody footprints on my roots. He turns the lights back on.

I smell him. Have to find out where he gets that cologne. I think it's called Fear. This is turning into one of those repeating nightmares where you keep falling but never hit the floor. Only I feel like I just smacked into the ground at a hundred miles an hour.

IT: "You seen Rachelle? Rachelle Bruin?"

I sit completely still. Maybe I can blend in with the metal tables and crumbling clay pots. He walks toward me, long, slow strides. The smell chokes me. I shiver.

IT: "She's supposed to meet me, but I can't find her anywhere. You know who she is?"

Me:

IT sits on my table, ITs leg smears my chalk drawing, blurring the roots into a mossy fog.

IT: "Hello? Anyone home? Are you deaf?"

IT stares at my face. I crush my jaws together so hard my teeth crumble to dust.

I am a deer frozen in the headlights of a tractor trailer. Is he going to hurt me again? He couldn't, not in school. Could he? Why can't I scream, say something, do anything? Why am I so afraid?

"Andy? I've been waiting outside." Rachel sweeps into the room wearing an artsy-fartsy gypsy scarf skirt and a necklace of eye-sized mirrors. She pouts and Andy leaps off the table, ripping my paper, scattering bits of chalk. Ivy walks through the door, bumping Rachel accidentally. She hesitates—she has to feel that something is going on—then she takes her sculpture off the shelf and sits at the table next to me. Rachel looks at me, but she doesn't say anything. She must have gotten my note—I mailed it over a week ago. I stand up. Rachel gives us a half wave and says "Ciao." Andy puts his arm around her waist and pulls her close to his body as they float out the door.

Ivy is talking to me, but it takes a while before I can hear her. "What a jerk," she says. She pinches the clay. "I can't believe she's going out with him. Can you? It's like I don't know her anymore. And he's trouble." She slaps a hunk of clay on the table. "Believe me, that creep is trouble with a capital T."

I'd love to stay and chat, but my feet won't let me. I walk home instead of taking the bus. I unlock the front door and walk straight up to my room, across the rug, and into my closet without even taking off my backpack. When I close the closet door behind me, I bury my face into the clothes on the left side of the rack, clothes that haven't fit for years. I stuff my mouth with old fabric and scream until there are no sounds left under my skin.

HOME SICK

It is time for a mental-health day. I need a day in pajamas, eating ice cream from the carton, painting my toenails, and enjoying TrashTV. You have to plan ahead for a mental-health day. I learned this from a conversation my mom had with her friend Kim. Mom always starts acting sick forty-eight hours ahead of time. She and Kim take mental-health days together. They buy shoes and go to the movies. Cutting-edge adult delinquency. What is the world coming to?

I don't eat any dinner or dessert, and I cough so much during the news my dad tells me to take some cough medicine. In the morning, I smear some mascara under my eyes so it looks like I haven't slept at all. Mom takes my temperature—turns out I have a fever. Surprises even me. Her hand is cool, an island on my forehead.

The words tumble out before I can stop them.

Me: "I don't feel well."

Mom pats my back.

Mom: "You must be sick. You're talking."

Even she can hear how bitchy that sounds. She clears her throat and tries again.

Mom: "I'm sorry. It's nice to hear your voice. Go back to bed. I'll bring up a tray before I leave. Do you want some ginger ale?"

I nod.

OPRAH, SALLY JESSY, JERRY, AND ME

My fever is 102.2. Sounds like a radio station. Mom calls to remind me to drink a lot of fluids. I say "Thank you," even though it hurts my throat. It's nice of her to call me. She promises to bring home Popsicles. I hang up and snuggle into my couch nest with the remote. Click. Click. Click.

If my life were a TV show, what would it be? If it were an After-School Special, I would speak in front of an auditorium of my peers on How Not to Lose Your Virginity. Or, Why Seniors Should Be Locked Up. Or, My Summer Vacation: A Drunken Party, Lies, and Rape.

Was I raped?

Oprah: "Let's explore that. You said no. He covered your mouth with his hand. You were thirteen years old. It doesn't matter that you were drunk. Honey, you were raped. What a horrible, horrible thing for you to live though. Didn't you ever think of telling anyone? You can't keep this inside forever. Can someone get her a tissue?"

Sally Jessy: "I want this boy held responsible. He is to blame for this attack. You do know it was an attack, don't you? It was not your fault. I want you to listen to me, listen to me, listen to me. It was not your fault. This boy was an animal."

Jerry: "Was it love? No. Was it lust? No. Was it tenderness, sweetness, the First Time they talk about in magazines? No, no, no, no, no! Speak up, Meatilda, ah, Melinda, I can't hear you!"

My head is killing me, my throat is killing me, my stomach bubbles with toxic waste. I just want to sleep. A coma would be nice. Or amnesia. Anything, just to get rid of this, these thoughts, whispers in my mind. Did he rape my head, too?

I take two Tylenol and eat a bowl of pudding. Then I watch *Mister Rogers' Neighborhood* and fall asleep. A trip to the Neighborhood of Make-Believe would be nice. Maybe I could stay with Daniel Striped Tiger in his tree house.

REAL SPRING

May is finally here and it has stopped raining. Good thing, too—the mayor of Syracuse was about to put out a call for a guy named Noah. The sun appears butter-yellow and so warm it coaxes tulips out of the crusty mud. A miracle.

Our yard is a mess. All our neighbors have these great magazine-cover yards with flowers that match their shutters and expensive white rocks that border fresh mounds of mulch. Ours has green bushes that just about cover the front windows, and lots of dead leaves.

Mom is already gone. Saturday is the biggest selling day of the week at Effert's. Dad snores upstairs. I put on old jeans and unearth a rake from the back of the garage. I start on the leaves suffocating the bushes. I bet Dad hasn't cleaned them out for years. They look harmless and dry on top, but under that top layer they're wet and slimy. White mold snakes from one leaf to the next. The leaves stick together like floppy pages in a decomposing book. I rake a mountain into the front yard and there are still more, like the earth pukes up leaf gunk when I'm not looking. I have to fight the bushes. They snag the tines of the rake and hold them—they don't like me cleaning out all that rot.

It takes an hour. Finally, the rake scrapes its metal fingernails along damp brown dirt. I get down on my knees to reach behind and drag out the last leaves. Ms. Keen would be proud of me. I observe. Worms caught in the sun squirm for cover. Pale green shoots of something alive have been struggling under the leaves. As I watch, they straighten to face the sun. I swear I can see them grow.

The garage door opens and Dad backs out the Jeep. He stops in the driveway when he sees me. He turns off the engine and gets out. I stand up and brush the dirt off my jeans. My palms are blistered and my arms are already sore from the raking. I can't tell if he's angry or not. Maybe he likes the front of his house looking like crap.

Dad: "That's a lot of work."

Me:

Dad: "I'll get some leaf bags at the store."

Me:

We both stand there with our arms crossed, staring at the little baby plants trying to grow in the shade of the house-eating bushes. The sun goes behind a cloud and I shiver. I should have worn a sweatshirt. The wind rustles dead leaves still clinging to the oak branches by the street. All I can think of is that the rest of the leaves are going to drop and I'll have to keep raking.

Dad: "Looks a lot better. Cleaned out like that, I mean."

The wind blows again. The leaves tremble.

Dad: "I suppose I should trim back the bushes. Of course, then you'd see the shutters and they need paint. And if I paint these shutters, I'll have to paint all the shutters, and the trim needs work, too. And the front door."

Me:

Tree: "Hush rustle chitachita shhhh . . ."

Dad turns to listen to the tree. I'm not sure what to do.

Dad: "And that tree is sick. See how the branches on the left don't have any buds? I should call someone to take a look at it. Don't want it crashing into your room during a storm."

Thanks, Dad. Like I'm not already having a hard time sleeping. Worry #64: flying tree limbs. I shouldn't have raked anything. Look what I started. I shouldn't have tried something new. I should have stayed in the house. Watched cartoons with a double-sized bowl of Cheerios. Should have stayed in my room. Stayed in my head.

Dad: "I guess I'm going to the hardware store. Want to come?"

The hardware store. Seven acres of unshaven men and bright-eyed women in search of the perfect screwdriver, weed killer, volcanic gas grills. Noise. Lights. Kids running down the aisle with hatchets and axes and saw blades. People fighting about the right color to paint the bathroom. No thank you.

I shake my head. I pick up the rake and start making the dead-leaf pile neater. A blister pops and stains the rake handle like a tear. Dad nods and walks to the Jeep, keys jangling in his fingers. A mockingbird lands on a low oak branch and scolds me. I rake the leaves out of my throat.

Me: "Can you buy some seeds? Flower seeds?"

FAULT!

Our gym teacher, Ms. Connors, is teaching us to play tennis. Tennis is the only sport that comes close to not being a total waste of time. Basketball would be great if all you had to do was shoot foul shots, but most of the time you're on the court with nine other people bumping and shoving and running way too much. Tennis is more civilized. Only two people have to play, unless you play doubles, which I would never do. The rules are simple, you get to catch your breath every few minutes, and you can work on your tan.

I actually learned to play a couple of summers ago when my parents had a trial membership at a fitness club. Mom signed me up for lessons and I played with Dad a few times before they figured the monthly dues were too expensive. Since I'm not a total spaz with the racket, Ms. Connors pairs me off with Jock Goddess Nicole to demonstrate the game to the rest of the class.

I serve first, a nice shot with a little speed on it. Nicole hits it right back to me with a great backhand. We volley a bit back and forth. Then Ms. Connors blows her whistle to stop and explain the retarded scoring system in tennis where the numbers don't make sense and love doesn't count for anything.

Nicole serves next. She aces it, a perfect serve at about ninety miles an hour that kisses the court just inside the line before I can move. Ms. Connors tells Nicole she's awesome and Nicole smiles.

I do not smile.

I'm ready for her second serve and I hit it right back down her throat. Ms. Connors says something nice to me and Nicole adjusts the strings on her racket. My serve.

I bounce the ball a few times. Nicole bounces on the balls of her feet. She isn't fooling around anymore. Her pride is at stake, her womynhood. She is not about to be beat by some weirdo hushquiet delinquent who used to be her friend. Ms. Connors tells me to hit the ball.

I slam into the ball, sending it right to Nicole's mouth, grinning behind her custom purple mouth guard. She twists out of the way.

Ms. Connors: "Fault!" Giggles from the class.

A foot fault. Wrong foot forward, toe over the line. I get a second chance. Another civilized aspect of tennis.

I bounce the yellow ball, one two three. Up in the air like releasing a bird or an apple, then arcing my arm, rotate shoulder, bring down the power and the anger and don't forget to aim. My racket takes on a life of its own, a bolt of energy. It crashes down on the ball, bulleting it over the net. The ball explodes on the court, leaving a crater before Nicole can blink. It blows past her and hits the fence so hard it rattles. No one laughs.

No fault. I score a point. Nicole wins eventually, but not by much. Everybody else whines about their blisters. I have calluses on my hands from yard work. I'm tough enough to play and strong enough to win. Maybe I can get Dad to practice with me a few times. It would be the only glory of a really sucky year if I could beat someone at something.

YEARBOOKS

The yearbooks have arrived. Everyone seems to understand this ritual but me. You hunt down every person who looks vaguely familiar and get them to write in your yearbook that the two of you are best friends and you'll never forget each other and remember _____ class (fill in the blank) and have a great summer. Stay sweet.

I watch some kids ask the cafeteria ladies to sign their books. What do they write: "Hope your chicken patties never bleed?" Or, maybe, "May your Jell-O always wiggle?"

The cheerleaders have obtained some sort of special exemption to roam the hall in a pack with pens in hand to seek out autographs of staff and students. I catch a whiff of competitive juices when they float past me. They are counting signatures.

The appearance of the yearbook clears up another high school mystery—why all the popular girls put up with the disgusting habits of Todd Ryder. He is a pig. Greasy, sleazy, foul-mouthed, and unwashed, he'll make a great addition to a state college fraternity. But the popular kids kissed up to him all year. Why?

Todd Ryder is the yearbook photographer.

Flip through the pages and see who is in his favor. Be nice to Todd and he'll take pictures of you that should have a modeling agency calling your house any day now. Snub Todd and you'll look like a trailer-park refugee having a bad hair day.

If I ran a high school, I would include stuff like this in the first-day indoctrination. I hadn't understood the Power of Todd. He snapped one picture of me, walking away from the camera wearing my dumpy winter coat, my shoulders up around my ears.

I will not be buying a yearbook.

HAIRWOMAN NO MORE

Hairwoman got a buzz cut. Her hair is half an inch long, a new crop of head fur, short and spiky. It's black—no fake orange at all. And she got new glasses, purple-rimmed bifocals that hang from a beaded chain.

I don't know what caused this. Has she fallen in love? Did she get a divorce? Move out of her parents' basement? You never think about teachers having parents, but they must.

Some kids say she did it to confuse us while we are working on our final essay. I'm not sure. We have a choice. We can write about "Symbolism in the Comics" or "How Story Changed My Life." I think something else is going on. I'm thinking she found a good shrink, or maybe she published that novel she's been writing since the earth cooled. I wonder if she'll be teaching summer school.

LITTLE WRITING ON THE WALL

Ivy is sitting at my art table with four uncapped colored markers sticking out of her bun. I stand up, she turns her head, and bingo—I've got a rainbow on my shirt. She apologizes a hundred million times. If it were anyone else, I would figure they did it on purpose. But Ivy and me have sort of been friendly the last few weeks. I don't think she was trying to be mean.

Mr. Freeman lets me go to the bathroom, where I try to scrub the stains. I must look like a dog chasing its tail, twisting and twirling, trying to see the stains on my back in the mirror. The door swings open. It's Ivy. I raise my hand as she opens her mouth. "Don't say it anymore. I know you're sorry. It was an accident."

She points to the pens still stuck in her bun. "I put the caps on. Mr. Freeman made me. Then he sent me in here to see how you're doing."

"He's worried about me?"

"He wants to make sure you don't pull a disappearing act. You have been known to wander off."

"Not in the middle of class."

"There's a first time for everything. Go in the stall and hand over your shirt. You can't wash it while you're wearing it."

I think Principal Principal should have his office in the rest room. Maybe then he'd hire somebody to keep it clean, or an armed guard to stop people from plugging up the toilet, smoking, or writing on the walls.

"Who is Alexandra?" I ask.

"I don't know any Alexandras," Ivy's voice says above the rush of water in the sink. "There might be an Alexandra in tenth grade. Why?"

"According to this, she has pissed off a whole bunch of people. One person wrote in huge letters that she's a whore, and all these others added on little details. She slept with this guy, she slept with that guy, she slept with those guys all at the same time. For a tenth-grader, she sure gets around."

Ivy doesn't answer. I peer through the crack between the door and the wall. She opens the soap container and dips my shirt in it. Then she scrubs the stains. I shiver. I'm standing in a bra, not a terribly clean bra, and it is freezing in here. Ivy holds the shirt up to the light, frowns, and scrubs some more. I want to take a deep breath, but it smells too bad.

"Remember what you said about Andy Evans being big trouble?"

"Yeah."

"Why did you say that?"

She rinses the soap from the shirt. "He has such a reputation. He's only after one thing, and if you believe the rumors, he'll get it, no matter what." She wrings the water out of the shirt. The sound of dripping water echoes off the tiles.

"Rachel is going out with him," I say.

"I know. Just add that to the list of stupid things she's done this year. What does she say about him?"

"We don't really talk," I say.

"She's a bitch, that's what you mean. She thinks she's too good for the rest of us."

Ivy punches the silver button on the hand dryer and holds up the shirt. I reread the graffiti. "I luv Derek." "Mr. Neck bites." "I hate this place." "Syracuse rocks." "Syracuse sucks." Lists of hotties, lists of jerks, list of ski resorts in Colorado everyone dreams about. Phone numbers that have been scratched out with keys. Entire conversations scroll down the bathroom stall. It's like a community chat room, a metal newspaper.

I ask Ivy to hand over one of her pens. She does. "I think you're going to have to bleach this thing," she says and hands over the shirt as well. I pull it over my head. It's still damp. "What did you want the marker for?"

I hold the cap in my teeth. I start another subject thread on the wall: *Guys to Stay Away From.* The first entry is the Beast himself: *Andy Evans.*

I swing open the door with a flourish. "Ta-da!" I point to my handiwork.

Ivy grins.

PROM PREPARATION

The climax of mating season is nearly upon us—the Senior Prom. They should cancel school this week. The only things we're learning are who is going with who (whom? must ask Hairwoman), who bought a dress in Manhattan, which limo company won't tell if you drink, the most expensive tux place, and on and on and on. The gossip energy alone could power the building's electricity for the rest of the marking period. The teachers are pissed. Kids aren't handing in homework because they have appointments at the tanning salon.

Andy Beast asked Rachel to go with him. I can't believe her mother is letting her go, but maybe she agreed because they're going to double with Rachel's brother and his date. Rachel is one of the rare ninth-graders invited to the Senior Prom; her social stock has soared. She must not have gotten my note, or maybe she decided to ignore it. Maybe she showed it to Andy and they had a good laugh. Maybe she won't get in the trouble I did, maybe he'll listen to her. Maybe I had better stop thinking about it before I go nuts.

Heather has come bellycrawling for help. My mother can't believe it: a living, breathing friend on the front porch for her

176

maladjusted daughter! I pry Heather out of Mom's claws and we retreat to my room. My stuffed rabbits crawl out of their burrows, noses awiggling, pink bunny, purple bunny, a gingham bunny from my grandma. They are as excited as my mother. Company! I can see the room through Heather's green-tinted contacts. She doesn't say anything, but I know she thinks it looks stupid—a baby room, all those toy rabbits; there must be a hundred of them. Mom knocks on the door. She has cookies for us. I want to ask if she's feeling sick. I hand the bag to Heather. She takes one cookie and nibbles at its edges. I snarf five, just to spite her. I lie on my bed, trapping the bunnies next to the wall. Heather delicately pushes a pile of dirty clothes off my chair and perches her skinny butt on it. I wait.

She launches into a sob story about how much she hates being a Marthadrone. Indentured servitude would be better. They are just taking advantage of her, bossing her around. Her grades are all the way down to Bs because of the time she has to spend waiting on her Senior Marthas. Her father is thinking about taking a job in Dallas and she wouldn't mind moving again, nope not one bit, because she's heard kids in the South aren't as stuck-up as they are here.

I eat more cookies. I'm fighting the shock of having a guest in my room. I almost kick her out because it's going to hurt too much when my room is empty again. Heather says I was smart, ". . . so smart, Mel, to blow off this stupid group. This whole year has been horrible—I hated every single day, but I didn't have the guts to get out like you did."

She completely ignores the fact that I was never in, and that she dumped me, banished me from even the shadows of Martha glory. I feel like any minute a guy in a lavender suit will burst into the room with a microphone and bellow, "Another alternate-reality moment brought to you by Adolescence!"

I still can't figure out why she's here. She licks a crumb off her cookie and gets to the point. She and the other Junior Marthas are required to decorate the Route 11 Holiday Inn ballroom for the prom. Meg 'n' Emily 'n' Siobhan can't assist, of course; they have to get their nails painted and their teeth whitened. The privileged, the few, the Junior Marthas have been laid waste by mononucleosis, leaving Heather all by herself. She is desperate.

Me: "You have to decorate the whole thing? By Saturday night?"

Heather: "Actually, we can't start until three o'clock Saturday afternoon because of some stupid meeting of Chrysler salesmen. But I know we can do it. I'm asking other kids, too. Do you know anyone who could help?"

Frankly, no I don't, but I chew and try to look thoughtful. Heather takes this to mean that yes, I'd be happy to help her. She bounces out of the chair.

Heather: "I knew you would help. You're great. Tell you what. I owe you, I owe you a big one. How about next week I come over and help you redecorate?"

178

Me:

Heather: "Didn't you tell me once how much you hated your room? Well, now I see why. It would be so depressing just to wake up here every morning. We'll clear out all this junk." She kicks a chenille bunny who was sleeping in my robe on the floor. "And get rid of those curtains. Maybe you could go shopping with me—can you get your mom's American Express?" She yanks my curtains to one side. "Let's not forget to wash those windows. Sea-foam green and sage, that's what you should look for, classic and feminine."

Me: "No."

Heather: "You want something richer, like an eggplant, or cobalt?"

Me: "No, I haven't decided on colors yet. That's not what I mean, I mean no, I won't help you."

She collapses into the chair again. "You have to help me."

Me: "No, I don't."

Heather: "But, whiii—iiiy?"

I bite my lip. Does she want to know the truth, that she's self-centered and cold? That I hope all the seniors yell at her? That I hate sea-foam green, and besides, it's none of her business if my windows are dirty? I feel tiny button noses against my back. Bunnies say to be kind. Lie.

Me: "I have plans. The tree guy is coming to work on the oak out front, I have to dig in my garden, and besides, I know what I want to do in here and it doesn't include eggplant."

Most of it is half true, half planned. Heather scowls. I open the dirty window to let in fresh air. It brushes my hair back off my face. I tell Heather she has to leave. I need to clean. She crams her cookie in her mouth and does not say goodbye to my mother. What a snot.

COMMUNICATION 101

I'm on a roll. I'm rocking. I don't know what it is; standing up to Heather, planting marigold seeds, or maybe the look on Mom's face when I asked if she would let me redecorate my room. The time has come to arm-wrestle some demons. Too much sun after a Syracuse winter does strange things to your head, makes you feel strong, even if you aren't.

I must talk to Rachel. I can't do it in algebra, and the Beast waits for her outside English. But we have study hall at the same time. Bingo. I find her squinting at a book with small type in the library. She's too vain for glasses. I instruct my heart not to bolt down the hall, and sit next to her. No nuclear bombs detonate. A good start.

She looks at me without expression. I try on a smile, size medium. "Hey," I say. "Hmm," she responds. No lip curling, no rude hand gestures. So far, so good. I look at the book she's copying (word for word) from. It's about France.

Me: "Homework?"

Rachel: "Kind of." She taps her pencil on the table. "I'm going to France this summer with the International Club. We have to do a report to prove we're serious."

Me: "That's great. I mean, you've always talked about traveling, ever since we were kids. Remember when we were in fourth grade and we read *Heidi* and we tried to melt cheese in your fireplace?"

We laugh a little too loudly. It's not really that funny, but we're both nervous. A librarian points his finger at us. Bad students, bad bad students. No laughing. I look at her notes. They are lousy, a few facts about Paris decorated with an Eiffel Tower doodle, hearts, and the initials R.B. + A.E. Gack.

Me: "So, you're really going out with him. With Andy. I heard about the prom."

Rachel grins honey-slow. She stretches, like the mention of his name wakes her muscles and makes her tummy jump. "He's great," she says. "He is just so awesome, and gorgeous, and yummy." She stops. She is talking to the village leper.

Me: "What are you going to do when he goes to college?"

Argh, an arrow to her soft spot. Clouds across the sun. "I can't think about that. It hurts too much. He said he was going to get his parents to let him transfer back here. He could go to La Salle or Syracuse. I'll wait for him."

Give me a break.

Me: "You've been going out for, like, what—two weeks? Three?"

A cold front blows across the library. She straightens up and snaps shut the cover of her notebook.

Rachel: "What do you want, anyway?"

Before I can answer, the librarian pounces. We are welcome to continue our conversation in the principal's office, or we can stay and be quiet. Our choice. I take out my notebook and write to Rachel.

It's nice to talk to you again. I'm sorry we couldn't be friends this year. I pass the notebook to her. She melts a bit around the edges and writes back.

Yeah, I know. So, who do you like?

No one, really. My lab partner is kinda nice, but like a friend-friend, not a boyfriend or anything.

Rachel nods wisely. She's dating a senior. She is so beyond these freshman "friend-friend" relationships. She's in charge again. Time for me to suck up.

Are you still mad at me? I write.

She doodles a quick lightning bolt.

No, I guess not. It was a long time ago. She stops and draws a spiraling circle. I stand on the edge and wonder if I'm going to fall in. *The party was a little wild*, she continues. *But it was dumb to call the cops. We could have just left.* She slides the notebook over to me.

I draw a spiraling circle in the opposite direction to Rachel's. I could leave it like this, stop in the middle of the highway. She's talking to me again. All I have to do is keep the dirt hidden and walk arm in arm with her into the sunset. She reaches back to fix her hair scrunchie. "R.B. + A.E." is written in red pen on the inside of her forearm. Breathe in, one-two-three. Breathe out, one-two-three. I force my hand to relax.

I didn't call the cops to break up the party, I write. *I called—*I put the pencil down. I pick it up again—*them because some guy raped me. Under the trees. I didn't know what to do.* She watches as I carve out the words. She leans closer to me. I write more. *I was stupid and drunk and I didn't know what was happening and then he hurt—*I scribble that out—*raped me. When the police came, everyone was screaming, and I was just too scared, so I cut through some back yards and walked home.*

I push the notebook back to her. She stares at the words. She pulls her chair around to my side of the table.

Oh my God, I am so sorry, she writes. *Why didn't you tell me?*

I couldn't tell anybody.

183

Does your mom know?

I shake my head. Tears pop up from some hidden spring. Damn. I sniff and wipe my eyes on my sleeve.

Did you get pregnant? Did he have a disease? Oh my God, Are you OK?????????

No. I don't think so. Yes, I'm OK. Well, kinda.

Rachel writes in a heavy, fast hand. *WHO DID IT???*

I turn the page.

Andy Evans.

"Liar!" She stumbles out of her chair and grabs her books off the table. "I can't believe you. You're jealous. You're a twisted little freak and you're jealous that I'm popular and I'm going to the prom and so you lie to me like this. And you sent me that note, didn't you? You are so sick."

She spins to take on the librarian. "I'm going to the nurse," she states. "I think I'm going to throw up."

CHAT ROOM

I'm standing in the lobby, looking at the buses. I don't want to go home. I don't want to stay here. I got my hopes up halfway through the conversation with Rachel—that was my mistake. It was like smelling the perfect Christmas feast and having the door slammed in your face, leaving you alone in the cold.

"Melinda." I hear my name. Great. Now I'm hearing things. Maybe I should ask the guidance counselor for a therapist or a nosy shrink. I don't say anything and I feel awful. I tell somebody and I feel worse. I'm having trouble finding a middle ground.

Someone touches my arm gently. "Melinda?" It's Ivy. "Can you take the late bus? I want to show you something." We walk together. She leads me to the bathroom, the one where she washed my shirt, which, by the way, still has traces of her markers, even after the bleach. She points to the stall. "Take a look."

GUYS TO STAY AWAY FROM

Andy Evans

He's a creep.

He's a bastard.

Stay away!!!

He should be locked up.

He thinks he's all that.

Call the cops.

What's the name of that drug they give perverts so they can't get it up?

Diprosomething.

He should get it every morning in his orange juice. I went out with him to the movies—he tried to get his hands down my pants during the PREVIEWS!!

There's more. Different pens, different handwriting, conversations between some writers, arrows to longer paragraphs. It's better than taking out a billboard.

I feel like I can fly.

PRUNING

I wake the next morning, Saturday, to the sound of a chain saw, the noise biting right through my ears and splintering my plans of sleeping in. I peer out the window. The arborists, the tree guys Dad called to trim the oak's dead branches, stand at the base of the tree, one guy revving up the chain saw like it's a sports car, the other giving the tree the once-over. I go downstairs for breakfast.

Watching cartoons is out of the question. I make a cup of tea and join Dad and a group of neighborhood kids watching the show from the driveway. One arborist monkeys his way into the pale green canopy, then hauls up the chain saw (turned off) at the end of a thick rope. He sets to work pruning the deadwood like a sculptor. "Brrrrr-rrrrowww." The chain saw gnaws through the oak, branches crashing to the ground.

The air swirls with sawdust. Sap oozes from the open sores on the trunk. He is killing the tree. He'll only leave a stump. The tree is dying. There's nothing to do or say. We watch in silence as the tree crashes piece by piece to the damp ground.

The chain-saw murderer swings down with a grin. He doesn't even care. A little kid asks my father why that man is chopping down the tree.

Dad: "He's not chopping it down. He's saving it. Those branches were long dead from disease. All plants are like that. By cutting off the damage, you make it possible for the tree to grow again. You watch—by the end of summer, this tree will be the strongest on the block."

I hate it when my father pretends to know more than he does. He sells insurance. He is not a forest ranger, wise in the way of the woods. The arborist fires up the mulcher at the back of their truck. I've seen enough. I grab my bike and take off.

The first stop is the gas station, to pump up my tires. I can't remember the last time I rode. The morning is warm, a lazy, slow Saturday. The parking lot at the grocery store is full. A couple of softball games are being played behind the elementary school, but I don't stop to watch. I ride up the hill past Rachel's house, past the high school. The down side is a fast, easy coast. I dare myself to lift my hands off the handlebars.

As long as I'm moving fast enough, the front wheel holds steady. I turn left and left again, following the hills down without realizing where I'm heading.

Some part of me has planned this, a devious internal compass pointed to the past. The lane isn't familiar until I glimpse the barn. I squeeze the brakes hard and struggle to control the bike on the gravel shoulder. A wind rips through the phone wires overhead. A squirrel fights to retain her balance.

There are no cars in the driveway. "Rodgers" is painted on the mailbox. A basketball hoop hangs off the side of the barn. I don't remember that, but it would have been hard to see it in the dark. I walk my bike along the back edge of the property to where the trees swallow the sun. My bike leans into a collapsing fence. I sink to the shade-cold ground.

My heart thuds as if I were still pedaling up the hill. My hands shake. It is a completely normal place, out of sight of the barn and house, close enough to the road that I can hear cars passing. Fragments of acorn shells litter the ground. You could bring a kindergarten class here for a picnic.

I think about lying down. No, that would not do. I crouch by the trunk, my fingers stroking the bark, seeking a Braille code, a clue, a message on how to come back to life after my long undersnow dormancy. I have survived. I am here. Confused, screwed up, but here. So, how can I find my way? Is there a chain saw of the soul, an ax I can take to my memories or fears? I dig my fingers into the dirt and squeeze. A small, clean part of me waits to warm and burst through the surface. Some quiet Melindagirl I haven't seen in months. That is the seed I will care for.

PROWLING

When I get home, it's time for lunch. I make two egg-salad sandwiches and drink an enormous glass of milk. I eat an apple and put my dishes in the dishwasher. It's only one o'clock. I suppose I should clean the kitchen and vacuum, but the windows are open and robins sing on the front lawn, where a pile of mulch with my name on it is waiting.

Mom is impressed when she drives up at dinnertime. The front lawn is raked, edged, mowed, and the bushes are mulched. I'm not even breathing hard. Mom helps me carry the plastic deck furniture up from the basement and I scrub it with bleach. Dad brings home pizza and we eat on the deck. Mom and Dad drink iced tea and there is no biting or snarling. I clear the dishes and throw the pizza box in the trash.

I lie down on the couch to watch TV, but my eyes close and I'm out. When I wake up, it's past midnight, and someone has covered me with an afghan. The house is quiet, dark. Cool breeze slides in between the curtains.

I am wide awake. I feel itchy inside my skin—antsy, that's what my mother would call it. I can't sit still. I have to do something. My bike is still leaning against the pruned tree in the front yard. I ride.

Up and down, across and diagonal, I pedal my sore legs through the streets of a suburb mostly sleeping. Some late-night TVs flicker from bedroom windows. A few cars are parked in front of the grocery store. I imagine people mopping the floors, restacking loaves of bread. I coast by the houses of people I used to know: Heather, Nicole. Turn the corner, downshift and pedal harder, up the hill to Rachel's house. The lights are on, her parents waiting for the fairy prom-goers to come home. I could knock on the door and ask them if they want to play cards or something. Nah.

I ride like I have wings. I am not tired. I don't think I'll ever have to sleep again.

POSTPROM

By Monday morning, the prom is legend. The drama! The tears! The passion! Why hasn't anyone made a television show out of this yet? The total damage included one stomach pumped, three breakups of long-term relationships, one lost diamond earring, four outrageous hotel-room parties, and five matching tattoos allegedly decorating the behinds of the senior class officers. The guidance counselors are celebrating the lack of fatal accidents.

Heather is not at school today. Everybody is griping about her lame decorations. I bet she calls in sick the rest of the year. Heather should run away and join the Marines immediately.

They'll be much sweeter to her than a swarm of angry Marthas.

Rachel is in her glory. She ditched Andy in the middle of the prom. I'm trying to piece the story together from grapevine gossip. They say she and Andy argued during a slow song. They say he was all over her with his hands and his mouth. While they danced, he was grinding against her and she backed off. The song ended and she swore at him. They say she was ready to slap him, but she didn't. He looked around, all innocent-like, and she stomped over to her exchange-student buddies. Ended up dancing the night away with a kid from Portugal. They say Andy's been really pissed off ever since. He got wicked drunk at a party and passed out in a bowl of bean dip. Rachel burned everything he ever gave her and left the ashes in front of his locker. His friends laughed at him.

Except for the gossip, there is no real point in coming to school. Well, there are final exams, but it's not like they are going to make any difference to my grades. We have—what? Two more weeks of classes? Sometimes I think high school is one long hazing activity: if you are tough enough to survive this, they'll let you become an adult. I hope it's worth it.

PREY

I'm waiting for the clock to end the daily torture-by-algebra session when WHAMMO!—a thought slams into my head: I don't want to hang out in my little hidy-hole anymore. I look behind me, half expecting to see a sniggering back-row guy who beaned me with an eraser. Nope—the back row is struggling to stay awake. It was definitely an idea that hit me. I don't feel like hiding anymore. A breeze from the open window blows my hair back and tickles my shoulders. This is the first day warm enough for a sleeveless shirt. Feels like summer.

After class, I trail behind Rachel. Andy is waiting for her. She won't even look at him. The kid from Portugal is now Rachel's numero uno. HA! Double HA! Serves you right, you scum. Kids stare at Andy, but nobody stops to talk. He follows Greta–Ingrid and Rachel down the hall. I am a few steps behind him. Greta–Ingrid spins around and tells Andy exactly what he should do to himself. Impressive. Her language skills have really improved this year. I'm ready to do a victory dance.

I head for my closet after school. I want to take the poster of Maya Angelou home, and I'd like to keep some of my tree pictures and my turkey-bone sculpture. The rest of the stuff can stay, as long as it doesn't have my name on it. Who knows, some other kids may need a safe place to run to next year.

Haven't been able to get rid of the smell. I leave the door cracked open a bit so I can breathe. It's hard to get the tree pictures off the walls without tearing them. The day is getting hotter and there's no circulation in here. I open the door wider—who's going to come by now? By this point in the year, teachers take off faster than students when the final bell rings. The only people left are a few teams scattered on the practice fields.

I don't know what to do with the comforter. It's really too ratty to take home. I should have gone to my locker first and gotten my backpack—I forgot about the books that are in here. I fold the comforter and set it on the floor, turn out the light, and head out the door for my locker. Somebody slams into my chest and knocks me back into the closet. The light flicks on and the door closes.

I am trapped with Andy Evans.

He stares at me without talking. He is not as tall as my memories, but is still loathsome. The lightbulb throws shadows under his eyes. He is made out of slabs of stone and gives off a smell that makes me afraid I'll wet my pants. He cracks his knuckles. His hands are enormous.

Andy Beast: "You have a big mouth, you know it? Rachel blew me off at the prom, giving me some bullshit story about how I raped you. You know that's a lie. I never raped anybody. I don't have to. You wanted it just as bad as I did. But your feelings got hurt, so you started spreading lies, and now every girl in school is talking about me like I'm some kind of pervert. You've been spreading that bullshit story for weeks. What's wrong, ugly, you jealous? Can't get a date?"

The words fall like nails on the floor, hard, pointed. I try to walk around him. He blocks my way. "Oh, no. You're not going anywhere. You really screwed things up for me." He reaches behind and locks the door. Click.

Me:

"You are one strange bitch, know that? A freak. I can't believe anyone listened to you." He grabs my wrists. I try to pull them back and he squeezes so tight it feels like my bones are splintering. He pins me against the closed door. Maya Angelou looks at me. She tells me to make some noise. I open my mouth and take a deep breath.

Beast: "You're not going to scream. You didn't scream before. You liked it. You're jealous that I took out your friend and not you. I think I know what you want."

His mouth is on my face. I twist my head. His lips are wet, his teeth knock against my cheekbone. I pull my arms again and he slams his body against mine. I have no legs. My heart wobbles. His teeth are on my neck. The only sound I can make is a whimper. He fumbles to hold both my wrists in one hand. He wants a free hand. I remember I remember. Metal hands, hot knife hands.

No.

A sound explodes from me.

"NNNOOO!!!"

I follow the sound, pushing off the wall, pushing Andy Evans off-balance, stumbling into the broken sink. He curses and turns, his fist coming, coming. An explosion in my head and blood in my mouth. He hit me. I scream, scream. Why aren't the walls falling? I'm screaming loud enough to make the whole school crumble. I grab for anything, my potpourri bowl—I throw it at him, it bounces to the floor. My books. He swears again. The door is locked the door is locked. He grabs me, pulls me away from the door, one hand over my mouth, one hand around my throat. He leans me against the sink. My fists mean nothing to him, little rabbit paws thumping harmlessly. His body crushes me.

My fingers wave overhead, looking for a branch, a limb, something to hang on to. A block of wood—the base of my turkey-bone sculpture. I slam it against Maya's poster. I hear a crunch. IT doesn't hear. IT breathes like a dragon. ITs hand leaves my throat, attacks my body. I hit the wood against the poster, and the mirror under it, again.

Shards of glass slip down the wall and into the sink. IT pulls away from me, puzzled. I reach in and wrap my fingers around a triangle of glass. I hold it to Andy Evans's neck. He freezes. I push just hard enough to raise one drop of blood. He raises his arms over his head. My hand quivers. I want to insert the glass all the way through his throat, I want to hear him scream. I look up. I see the stubble on his chin, a fleck of white in the corner of his mouth. His lips are paralyzed. He cannot speak. That's good enough.

Me: "I said no."

He nods. Someone is pounding on the door. I unlock it, and the door swings open. Nicole is there, along with the lacrosse team—sweaty, angry, their sticks held high. Someone peels off and runs for help.

FINAL CUT

Mr. Freeman is refusing to hand his grades in on time. They should have been in four days before the end of school, but he didn't see the sense in that. So I'm staying after school on the very, very last day for one last try at getting my tree right.

Mr. Freeman is covering the grade wall with a mural. He hasn't touched the line with my name, but he eliminated everything else with a roller brush and fast-drying white paint. He hums as he mixes colors on his palette. He wants to paint a sunrise.

Summer-vacation voices bubble through the open window. School is nearly over. The hall echoes with slamming lockers and shrieks of "I'm gonna miss you—got my number?" I turn up the radio.

My tree is definitely breathing; little shallow breaths like it just shot up through the ground this morning. This one is not perfectly symmetrical. The bark is rough. I try to make it look as if initials had been carved in it a long time ago. One of the lower branches is sick. If this tree really lives someplace, that branch better drop soon, so it doesn't kill the whole thing. Roots knob out of the ground and the crown reaches for the sun, tall and healthy. The new growth is the best part.

Lilac flows through the open windows with a few lazy bees. I carve and Mr. Freeman mixes orange and red to get the right shade of sunrise. Tires squeal out of the parking lot, another sober student farewell. I'm staring summer school in the face, so there's no real hurry. But I want to finish this tree.

A couple of seniors stroll in. Mr. Freeman hugs them carefully, either because of the paint on him or because teachers hugging students can make for big trouble. I shake my bangs down in front of my face and watch through my hair. They chat about New York City, where the girls are going to college. Mr. Freeman writes down some phone numbers and names of restaurants. He says he has plenty of friends in Manhattan and that they should meet for brunch some Sunday. The girls—the women—hop up and down and squeal, "I can't believe it's really happening!" One of them is Amber Cheerleader. Go figure.

The seniors look my way before they leave. One girl, not the cheerleader, nods her head, and says, "Way to go. I hope you're OK." With hours left in the school year, I have suddenly become popular. Thanks to the big mouths on the lacrosse team, everybody knew what happened before sundown. Mom took me to the hospital to stitch up the cut on my hand. When we got home, there was a message on the machine from Rachel. She wants me to call her.

My tree needs something. I walk over to the desk and take a piece of brown paper and a finger of chalk. Mr. Freeman talks about art galleries and I practice birds—little dashes of color on paper. It's awkward with the bandage on my hand, but I keep trying. I draw them without thinking—flight, flight, feather, wing. Water drips on the paper and the birds bloom in the light, their feathers expanding promise.

IT happened. There is no avoiding it, no forgetting. No running away, or flying, or burying, or hiding. Andy Evans raped me in August when I was drunk and too young to know what was happening. It wasn't my fault. He hurt me. It wasn't my fault. And I'm not going to let it kill me. I can grow.

I look at my homely sketch. It doesn't need anything. Even through the river in my eyes I can see that. It isn't perfect and that makes it just right.

The last bell rings. Mr. Freeman comes to my table.

Mr. Freeman: "Time's up, Melinda. Are you ready?"

I hand over the picture. He takes it in his hands and studies it. I sniff again and wipe my eyes on my arm. The bruises are vivid, but they will fade.

Mr. Freeman: "No crying in my studio. It ruins the supplies. Salt, you know, saline. Etches like acid." He sits on the stool next to me and hands back my tree. "You get an A+. You worked hard at this." He hands me the box of tissues. "You've been through a lot, haven't you?"

The tears dissolve the last block of ice in my throat. I feel the frozen stillness melt down through the inside of me, dripping shards of ice that vanish in a puddle of sunlight on the stained floor. Words float up.

Me: "Let me tell you about it."

HERE'S THE THING . . .

In late 1996, I woke up from a nightmare, thinking about the character who would become Melinda Sordino in *Speak*. I never thought the book would be published, but it was. More than a million people have read it. Go figure.

A couple of times a week for the last twelve years, readers have asked me when I'll be writing a sequel to *Speak*.

No. That's not entirely correct.

A couple of times a *day*, nearly every day for the last twelve years, readers have asked me when I'll be writing a sequel to *Speak*. Many of them have given helpful plot ideas. I could write about the trial, when Andy Evans is convicted of Melinda's rape and sent to jail. I could write about Melinda's therapy sessions, in which she confronts her parents for their emotional neglect. Or I could have her face a new trauma: she could start smoking meth, or develop amnesia after a car accident, or be kidnapped by a cult of perverts, or, or, or . . .

My favorite suggestion came from a ninth-grade boy in Southern California who told me I should write about how she got through the rest of high school without killing anyone. And I should call the sequel *Spoke*.

Actually, that's not such a bad idea.

Here's the thing: most sequels suck. Take a look (if you dare) at *Jurassic Park 2, Jaws: The Revenge*, or *Rambo 15*. Sequels are too often crass attempts to make money off something that worked the first time, but without the care and attention that made the first movie or book so special.

Book sequels seem to work best when the author had planned a follow-up from the beginning and left a few story lines dangling that could be picked up and woven into a new plot. Yes, I know I didn't wrap up everything at the end of *Speak*. I rarely do in my books. I like my last pages to be somewhat open-ended because that's the way things are in real life.

But despite all of that, here's another thing: I'm seriously thinking about writing a sequel. I've been thinking about it for a very long time. I loved writing about Melinda and it would be wonderful to hang out with her again. We caught a glimpse of her in *Catalyst*, but we saw her through the eyes of another character, Kate Malone. She couldn't tell us what was going on inside Melinda's heart.

I sometimes feel like Melinda is hiding in another closet, this time in my mind. She's waiting for me to find the right path to her door. The questions swirl. How serious is her relationship with David Petrakis? Will she ever have a girl friend she can trust? Is art her only salvation, or will she join the basketball team? Are her parents going to split up? Would she be happier if they did, or would that shatter her? What does she want to do after high school?

So here's the last thing: I can't write the sequel until I stumble on the right story and Melinda wakes me up again in the middle of the night. So it might never happen. Or it could happen next year. Or more likely, somewhere in between those two possibilities.

I'll speak up when Melinda is ready.

LAURIE HALSE ANDERSON
SPEAKS ABOUT SPEAK . .

How did the character of Melinda come to you?

In a nightmare! I woke up one night—panicked—because I could hear a girl sobbing. I checked on my daughters, but they were sound asleep. The crying girl was in my head, a bad dream. I sat down at the computer and wrote out what I was hearing. The next morning I listened to that voice again and the character of Melinda Sordino unfolded. When I first started writing, I had no idea what had happened to her. It wasn't until she was comfortable with me that she let her secret out.

What was the writing and revision process like?

The voice of Melinda was very strong throughout. At first, I toyed with the idea of making her totally mute, but in this day and age that would have led to medical and psychological interventions. I decided it was better to have her just withdraw and speak as little as possible. There are lots of kids out there in Melinda's position—struggling with depression and teetering on the edge of disaster—but people don't pay attention unless they do something drastic. This makes me so angry I could scream . . . or better yet, write a book.

The revision process focused on structure, on making Melinda's struggle and growth unfold at the right pace as the school year moved on. The holiday scenes are some of my favorites. The ending required a lot of time. I had three other endings that were all pathetic and lame. I had to really push myself and Melinda to find the right way to end the book. I'm very happy with it now.

The character of Heather from Ohio was originally two characters. As I revised, I realized that the girls each played the same role, so I combined them into one. Mr. Freeman's character felt flat in the early drafts, so I gave him his own piece of art to struggle with in the hope that it would deepen his character.

Your dialogue is dead-on—how do you capture the internal and external voices of high school students so well?

These days it is very easy because my house has been overrun by teenagers. When I wrote *Speak*, however, my kids were in elementary school. To get a sense of the rhythm of high school speech, I spent a lot of time at Taco Bell and the food court at the mall. We won't talk about what those field trips did to my waistline. . . .

I also found a piece of Melinda's voice in my own high school experience. Emotions don't change much from generation to generation. You just have to get the details right.

So how much of Melinda is based on you?

My freshman year in high school kind of resembled Melinda's. My family had moved the summer before, and I started ninth grade without knowing anyone. Things were complicated by the fact that my family was going through a small nuclear meltdown. My father had quit his job for some very good reasons, but he was wretchedly unhappy. Money was tight, we were in a new place, and the world felt foreign and scary to me. On the positive side, feeling isolated gave me (and Melinda) a useful perspective on the absurdities of high school culture.

A couple of the incidents from *Speak* were taken right out of my real life. I was the obnoxious kid in English class who grilled my teacher about symbolism and refused to accept her answer. My father buried several toxic stew experiments in the backyard (honest). And the real-life mascot of my high school was (and is) a hornet. And yes, we used to sing the Horny Hornet chant, though the cheerleaders did not have a special dance, nor were we ever videotaped by a television station.

What has been the biggest surprise since the book was published?

That so many people like it.

What have you learned from your readers' reactions to this book?

I've learned that *Speak* is not just a book about rape. *Speak* is a book about depression. That is why it has resonated so deeply for so many readers. Today's teens have to cope with massive amounts of stress and conflict. Way too many of them understand the pain of not feeling like they can speak up. This book reflects their experience and offers them hope.

What did you think of the movie? What can you tell us about it?

The movie is very faithful to the book, but obviously, some things had to be cut. If they had filmed the whole book, it would have been a twelve-hour movie. I was offered a chance to work on the screenplay, which I turned down because of other writing obligations. The screenplay was co-written by director Jessica Sharzer and Annie Young, the woman who spent several years fighting to get the book made into a movie.

I was on the set for a couple days, with my oldest daughter, Stephanie. It was a very moving, fun experience for both of us. The cast and crew were sweet, though I found that whenever Mr. Neck walked in the room, my stomach started to hurt. Even though he was sweet off camera, his on-camera role was intense—he nailed it. Everybody nailed it. Melinda, David, Mr. Freeman—they all rock this movie hard. One unknown actress gave a stunning, if brief, performance in her role as The Lunch Lady Who Puts Mashed Potatoes on the Plate. Yes, folks, that was me. Watch quickly. I'm on camera for almost a full second. Kristen Stewart, the actress who plays Melinda, had the most difficult job—showing a character's emotions without speaking much. She pulled it off perfectly.

I love the movie. A lot. Jessica did a fantastic job. She had a budget of one million dollars (*Twilight* had an estimated budget of 37 million), one camera, and three weeks to make the movie. They filmed it in Columbus, Ohio, during a killer heat wave. The air conditioning in the building had to be turned off because the noise messed up the sound recording. A record-breaking thunderstorm opened up holes in the school's roof—over the room that held all the electrical boxes—and they lost power for a day. I have no idea how Jessica pulled it off, but she did.

What are your Speak ***movie-watching tips?***

Lots of readers have held *Speak* movie parties. If you want to do that, here are some games to play while you're watching:

- Count how many times Melinda speaks.
- Watch for lines that came from the book.
- Figure out what famous teen movie the director paid homage to in one of the cafeteria scenes.

- Throw popcorn at the TV whenever IT shows up.
- Figure out what scenes were *not* in the book.
- Speculate on why the director chose the ending she did.

You can also play Spot the Food:

- Ho-Hos
- Mashed potatoes
- Powdered doughnuts
- Pop-Tarts
- Very bad turkey soup
- Pizza
- Applesauce

If you have read *Catalyst* in addition to *Speak*, award yourself five points and add these to your menu:

- Jell-O salad (preferably with fruit and nuts mixed in)
- Cheetos®

Have any readers ever asked questions that shocked you?

I have gotten one question repeatedly from young men. These are guys who liked the book, but they are honestly confused. They ask me why Melinda was so upset about being raped.

The first dozen times I heard this, I was horrified. But I heard it over and over again. I realized that many young men are not being taught the impact that sexual assault has on a woman. They are inundated by sexual imagery in the media, and often come to the (incorrect) conclusion that having sex is not a big deal. This, no doubt, is why the number of sexual assaults is so high.

I am also shocked by adults who feel that rape is an inappropriate topic to discuss with teenagers. According to the U.S. Department of Justice, 44 percent of rape victims are under the age of 18 and 46 percent of those victims are between the ages of 12–15. It makes adults uncomfortable to acknowledge this, but our inability to speak clearly and openly about sexual issues endangers our children. It is immoral not to discuss this with them.

How do you feel about your book being taught in so many middle schools, high schools, and colleges?

I was not a great English student in high school, so it makes me chuckle. It also gives me hope. I am really happy that today's English teachers are using contemporary literature in the classroom. I think the reason I didn't like English was because I couldn't stand the books we had to read. They were all about boring, middle-aged people a hundred years earlier. *Gack.*

Too many kids are turned off reading by being forced to read and regurgitate books that have no connection to their lives. I applaud the school districts and teachers who are bold and smart enough to find literature that helps their students grow as readers, and mature into thoughtful, caring people.

If I e-mail you the essay questions my teacher gave me for Speak, *will you e-mail me back with some tips about how to answer them?*

No way. One of the advantages of being an adult is never having to do homework again. However, if you go to my Web site— www.madwomanintheforest.com—you'll find lots of resources for all of my books. Also, check out the archives of my blog— halseanderson.livejournal.com. I do answer questions submitted to the blog, and you might find what you are looking for in the archives.

Do many survivors talk to you about their sexual assault stories? How do you deal with that?

I have heard from hundreds and hundreds of survivors of sexual assault, male as well as female. I always feel honored when they trust me with their stories. It can be emotionally hard to listen to them, but it doesn't begin to measure up to the pain the survivor has endured. My job in these situations is to listen carefully, reassure, and urge the person talking to me to find other trustworthy adults (parent, clergy, counselor, teacher) to talk to so they can get the help and resources they need.

What would you say to someone who has just been sexually assaulted?

The Rape, Abuse & Incest National Network—www.rainn.org —has the best resources around. It has advice for victims who were just assaulted, as well as advice for victims who were assaulted a while ago and who are struggling to find the courage to speak up about what happened, and get the help they all deserve to heal from the rape.

What message were you trying to send with this book?

I don't send messages. I try to tell good stories. But if you like a book and it is well written, you usually learn a couple of things. Good books reflect the human experience, and we all learn from that.

When did you know you wanted to be a writer? What do you love best about it? What's most difficult?

I have always written for fun. I sold some short stories in my late twenties, then conned my way through a series of newspaper and freelance writing jobs. It still stuns me that people will pay me to write. I keep waiting for someone to poke me in the shoulder and announce that a mistake was made, and I have to go back and milk cows again. (That's what I did to earn money for college.)

The most difficult thing about being an author is creating the uninterrupted time I need to think. Real life intrudes with alarming frequency. I also hate it when people ask when I'm going to get a "real job." And I think there should be a constitutional amendment prohibiting telemarketing. Other than that, writing is great.

I love letting my imagination take off—sometimes it returns home holding disgusting things in its mouth, but sometimes it brings back the good stuff! I love that kids like my books. I love coming up with just the right description, or action, or line of dialogue. The very best part of writing is figuring out how all the narrative threads and imagery connect. Watching a character take over the story is pretty cool, too.

What is your writing process? Is there a special place where you write?

I have written in a lot of different places. My first writing space was a closet (honest!). Then I moved to the basement, which was a bad idea. Very depressing. I've written in cities, in suburbs, airplanes, trains, and in the car during countless soccer and basketball practices.

Now I live out in the country and I work up in the attic of the house that my husband built. Behind my chair is the stone fireplace, overhead are the wooden beams that hold up the roof.

I try to wake up before dawn, go for a walk or a run as the sun is coming up, then get right to work. I write as many hours every day that I can, at least eight, and sometimes as many as twelve or sixteen. My first drafts are always very rough, but that's okay. My favorite part of writing is the revision process; I love the sensation of finally nailing a scene after fussing with it for weeks.

My life is my work and my work is my life. I don't really think of writing as a job; it's who I am.

You write a variety of books for all ages—from picture books to nonfiction to series fiction to historicals, in addition to contemporary YA [young adult]. There aren't many authors with your range. Can you tell us about this? Will you continue to write in such diverse genres?

I have a short attention span and I get bored easily. I love kids, all kids, from toddlers to teens. And I have *lots* of voices echoing in my head. Some are obviously teenagers, others are younger kids who want their stories heard. And nonfiction is interesting because it is a fun challenge to present facts in a way that will excite a reader. Over the course of a year, I'll average one novel for teens and one book for younger readers. As a writer, I love figuring out how to appeal to readers who are at different stages in their development. I can't imagine what it is like to only write for one age group. I would probably break out in a hideous rash if someone forced me to limit myself like that.

Are any of your books based on your family?

My husband and I have four kids. Right now (early 2009), two have graduated from college, a third is about to graduate, and the youngest is a junior in high school. I really love my kids a lot, and I would never put them in a book. That would be exploitation.

Do your kids like having a mom/stepmom who is an author?

They like the fact that I have a flexible schedule, and that we have so many books in our house. They do not like me when I am on deadline and writing twelve hours a day. And they wish I made more money.

What do you do in your spare time?

I don't have much of it. If I'm not hanging out with my husband or traveling, I'm either reading or writing. I like to work out at the gym and watch football and basketball. I enjoy fiddling with my Web site (www.madwomanintheforest.com). I really like to sleep. I wish I had more time for that.

Are you going to write a sequel to Speak?

This is a complicated question, so I wrote an entire essay about it. See "Here's the thing. . . ."

Why don't you ever write a book that has a boy as the main character?

I did! It's called *Twisted*. I was a little nervous about trying to write from a guy's point of view, but it wound up being a blast. Boys are fascinating creatures.

I've gotten a lot of heart-wrenching mail from boys about *Twisted*. Many of the letters are like this one:

"I just wanted to say thank you for writing this book. I have been considering killing myself for many years and . . . [this book] has given me a new perspective on life and that death isn't the easy way out. I can relate to Tyler in many ways for years. . . . I greatly appreciate this book because now I know that there is hope in my life and that death is not the answer. And one more thing this is the only book I have been able to pick up and not put down from start to finish."

That is what makes me get up before dawn every day, climb up to my attic, and work on the next book.

A COMMENT ABOUT CENSORSHIP

These are scary days in which to raise teenagers. I know. I've had four of them. Part of the problem is that we have a generation that has been exposed to unprecedented amounts of sexual behavior in the media and on the Internet. They see it, they talk about it, their hormones react, and a lot of kids wind up in painful situations.

Literature is the safe and traditional vehicle through which we learn about the world and pass on values from one generation to the next. Books save lives.

Contemporary young adult literature surprises some people, because it is an accurate reflection of the way today's teenagers talk, think, and behave. But these books must be honest in order to connect to the teen reader. America's teens are desperate for responsible, trustworthy adults to create situations in which they can discuss the issues that are of the highest concern for them. Reading and discussing books is one of the most effective ways to get teens to think through and learn about the challenges of adolescence.

Most of the censorship I see is fear-driven. I respect that. The world is a very scary place. It is a terrifying place in which to raise children, and in particular, teenagers. It is human nature to nurture and protect children as they grow into adulthood. But censoring books that deal with difficult, adolescent issues does not protect anybody. Quite the opposite. It leaves kids in darkness and makes them vulnerable.

Censorship is the child of fear and the father of ignorance. Our children cannot afford to have the truth of the world withheld from them. They need us to be brave enough to give them great books so they can learn how to grow up into the men and women we want them to be.

DISCUSSION GUIDE

- Discuss the title of the novel and its significance. What roles do silence and truth play in the story?

- Is there a relationship between speaking and listening? Can one exist without the other?

- What is friendship? Describe the important elements of Melinda's relationships with Heather, Ivy, Nicole, and Rachel. Is she ever really friends with any of them? Can friendship mean something different to different people? Cite different passages in the novel as evidence of your opinion.

- Melinda says: "It is easier not to say anything. Shut your trap, button your lip, can it. All that crap you hear on TV about communication and expressing feelings is a lie. Nobody really wants to hear what you have to say." Do you agree with her? Why or why not? Do the events in the novel support or negate her statement? Does her outlook change at any point in the novel? How so?

- What keeps Melinda silent? What is she afraid of?

- Discuss the social hierarchy of Merryweather High. What role does the concept of identity play in the novel? Why is belonging to one of the many clans so important to Heather and so unimportant to Melinda?

- Why does Melinda isolate herself from her friends? Is she justified in doing so?

- Melinda nicknames many of the other characters throughout the novel. Discuss the significance of this habit and how it contributes to the development of the story and your experience as a reader.

- Why do you think Melinda refers to Andy Evans as IT in the beginning of the novel? At what point does she start to call him by name? Why?

- In what places is Melinda able to find sanctuary at school? How do the characteristics of these places provide a window into her character?

- What does Melinda learn in art class? What does the tree she spends the year creating finally come to symbolize?

- How does David Petrakis contribute to Melinda's quest to find her voice? How does Mr. Freeman influence her? What role do her parents and the other adults in the novel play in Melinda's journey?

- Despite her internal sense of humor, Melinda seems depressed to the outside world. In what ways is her depression evident? How do the people around her react to her behavior? Do you think they respond appropriately? How would you respond?

- What role does rumor play in the story? Discuss how rumors and truth can be connected. Is one more powerful than the other?

- Reflect on Melinda and Rachel's written conversation they have in the library. Discuss Rachel's reaction to what Melinda tells her. Why do you think she behaves as she does? Does she believe Melinda?

- How does nature manifest itself in the story line and contribute to meaning? Discuss how the changing of the seasons could be argued to mirror Melinda's ability to speak.

- Is it possible to speak without spoken words? Why or why not? Identify passages in the novel to support your position.

- Discuss the ending of the book and the relevance of the last scene.

- What finally allows Melinda to speak?

SEXUAL ASSAULT SURVIVOR RESOURCES

<u>YOU ARE NOT ALONE.</u>

1 in 6 American women will be the victim of an attempted or completed rape. In the U.S., a rape is reported every five minutes. Experts estimate that only 16 percent of all rapes are ever reported to police.

Nearly half of rape and sexual assault victims are girls under the age of 18.

Girls between the ages of 16 and 19 are 4 times more likely than the general population to be victims of rape, attempted rape, or sexual assault.

Most teenagers who are raped or sexually assaulted are attacked by someone they know.

17.7 million American women have been victims of attempted or completed rape.

<u>MEN AND BOYS CAN BE SEXUALLY ASSAULTED, TOO.</u>

1 out of every 33 American men will be the victim of an attempted or completed rape.

In 2003, 10 percent of rape victims were male.

<u>VICTIMS OF SEXUAL ASSAULT ARE:</u>

3 times more likely to suffer from depression.
6 times more likely to suffer from post-traumatic stress disorder.
13 times more likely to abuse alcohol.
26 times more likely to abuse drugs.
4 times more likely to contemplate suicide.

*Statistics from studies by the Department of Justice and the Centers for Disease Control and Prevention—
see http://www.911rape.org/facts-quotes/statistics*

{more statistics: http://www.musc.edu/vawprevention/}

YOU DESERVE COMPASSION, UNDERSTANDING AND HELP.

RAINN (Rape, Abuse & Incest National Network)
www.rainn.org

SOAR (Speaking Out Against Rape) www.soar99.org

NSVRC (National Sexual Violence Resource Center)
www.nsvrc.org

Rape Treatment Center www.911rape.org

National Sexual Assault Hotline: 1.800.656.HOPE